THE OTHER SIDE OF TIME

Essays by "The Catskill Geologist"

Robert Titus, PhD

PURPLE MOUNTAIN PRESS
Fleischmanns, New York

This one is for the grandsons.

The Other Side of Time: Essays by "The Catskills Geologist"

Published by Purple Mountain Press, Ltd.
1060 Main Street, P.O. Box 309
Fleischmanns, New York 12430-0309
845-254-4062, 845-254-4476 (fax), purple@catkill.net
http://www.catskill.net/purple

ISBN 1-930098-82-0
ISBN-13 978-1-930098-82-4

Library of Congress Control Number: 2007935249

The chapters in this book were previously published in *Kaatskill Life: A Regional Journal*,
Delhi, New York; *Woodstock Times*, Woodstock, New York; *The Independent*, Hillsdale,
New York; *Greenville Press*, Greenville, New York, and are used by permission.

Manufactured in the United States of America.
Printed on acid-free paper.

Contents

Part Five: The Ice Age

Acknowledgments

I can never give enough thanks to the editors of *Kaatskill Life* and my several newspapers for all of their endlessly patient help with the nearly 300 manuscripts that I have sent in for their review. From *Kaatskill Life* magazine, Marilyn Milow Francis has always been extremely supportive and Nina Lawford-Juviler has composed layouts that have made my articles always look good. Parry Teasdale, editor of *The Independent* in Columbia County, gave me my first chance at newspaper work. Marcia Stamell, also of *The Independent*, is another of those remarkably supportive editors who have helped me to dramatically improve my work. Linda Fenoff has helped me with my work of my hometown paper, the *Greenville Press*.

I have shared an enthusiasm for our Catskills on hikes and excursions with too many people throughout the Catskills to acknowledge their inspiration in the making of this book. I will pick out Bob Gildersleeve, the Catskill's premier hiker, to represent all of them. Three generations of secretaries at Hartwick College's Science Division have advised me on grammar, syntax, and punctuation. I thank Sharon French, Suzanne Dudley and Nancy Heffernan for greatly improving my writing skills.

I owe a great deal to my wife Johanna who has gone thumping about in the Catskills with me, as we did so much of the field work together. Johanna has been my first and best editor since our marriage.

Introduction

IT'S been more than 15 years now since I began writing popular articles for *Kaatskill Life* magazine, and the experience has transformed my life. I have branched out, and I have now written regularly for four newspapers as well as the magazine. This is unusual. I know of no similar geology columnist, anywhere. And that is such a shame. Geology is a science that translates so well into the everyday experience of average people. It's all around us, and it is very visible. It has been a real pleasure and privilege to take people on "excursions" into this, my science.

I like to say that, as a geologist, I live in three different worlds and that might make a good theme for this book. The first of these "worlds" is the everyday one that all of us experience. In the Catskills that is a very nice world indeed, as we possess an extremely scenic landscape. But there are those two other worlds, and most people miss them. The second is the one preserved in the bedrock. Bedrock exposures are everywhere, and each one of them can take a person back through time. No matter where you are on the face of the Earth, your location, its longitude and latitude, has had a four-and-one-half-billion year history. That never fails to awe me. The spot where you are sitting now was here a century ago and a millennium ago too. Your spot was different at those moments of time. Your spot was also here a hundred million years ago. What was it like then? How about a billion years ago? We have lost almost all of your spot's history; so much has happened exactly where you are sitting, but we just will never know exactly what. It's sad.

But there are slivers of time that have been preserved. If you can read the rocks, they will tell you about those moments. Here in the Catskills there are stories of ancient oceans that were once here. Great mountains rose above our horizons. Vast delta complexes with all the floods, and dense tangled plant life that such habitats bring into being, were once here. And our rocks tell us about those moments. Much of this anthology takes us for those journeys through time to my geological "second world."

It is the landscape itself that takes us into the third world. The landscape "wears" the scars of the most recent moments of our geologic history. The events of the last few tens of thousands of years are well preserved if you know what to look for. And that takes us back to the Ice Age. That wonderful event is a godsend to the geology columnist. The glaciers brought all sorts of grand imagery to our Catskills and Hudson Valley. Just imagine for a moment the fact that there were once thousands of feet of glacial ice right here. Then (it actually gets better!) there was a very quick melting of all that ice. The advancing glaciers sculpted much of the landscape around us. Then the powerful meltwater streams finished the job. The results were much of the scenery that has brought millions of visitors to the Catskills.

That first world has become much more important to my writing since I started. It should not be surprising that I did very little writing about environmental geology back when I first began at *Kaatskill Life*. All my early articles were about classical geology. Now things have changed; environmental geology looms large on my profession's horizons. Many of the graduates at our Hartwick College Geology Department go into that field. Not surprisingly there is a great deal of interest in the environment among my readers. So, I have a section in this book devoted to the topic.

I am glad to offer this anthology. It gives me a chance to pick out my favorite articles and to put them all together in one volume. The sad thing about being a magazine and newspaper columnist is that past issues get old quickly and get thrown away. Here I have a chance to make some of my work a little more permanent.

This book is not meant to be taken too seriously. It is not a scientific tome; it is for the shear pleasure of living and hiking about in the Catskills and adjacent Hudson Valley and understanding something of the history that is right in front of you. Read it and learn some of the genuine joy that comes from being a geologist.

FREEHOLD, JUNE 5, 2007

PART ONE
Catskill Things and Catskill Places

BOYHOOD ROCK

EVERY ANCIENT ROCK has a story within it that can be read if you just know how. As a geologist, I learned long ago how to read these tales of the distant past. So it was no surprise that, upon visiting Boyhood Rock, I found a story worth repeating. One of the Catskills' best-known rocks, it's in the field just above Woodchuck Lodge, John Burroughs' summer retreat on a mountain called Old Clump in Roxbury.

The boulder, which is now Burroughs' tombstone, is special and its story deserves a full telling. Burroughs knew part of the story himself, as geology was his favorite science during his later years. He knew that the boulder was what's called a glacial erratic. It was carried here perhaps 22,000 years ago by the advancing ice of the Wisconsin Glaciation. Burroughs took great pleasure in understanding the glacial history of Old Clump. There is a picture of him showing the ice age evidence to Thomas Edison. All this I knew before my visit, but I was curious about the older history of the rock, the story of how it formed originally.

The rock is typical Catskill river sandstone, and it is of the Devonian Period, dating from nearly 400 million years ago. The sand was deposited one layer (or stratum) at a time, each representing a single moment of time. I found that many of these strata dipped steeply, with different sets of the strata dipping at sharply different angles, especially at the bottom of Boyhood Rock. These types of strata make up what's called cross-bedded sandstone. They formed in the deepest, fastest flowing parts of a stream channel. The several sets of strata may record episodes of flooding. One can imagine newspaper headlines shouting the news of terrible floods. There were, however, no newspapers during the Devonian; such stories were only recorded in stone.

The boulder is from the Oneonta Formation which makes up the bedrock of the upper Pepacton Valley. The Oneonta sandstones are, for the most part, river deposits of the old Catskill Delta. The fossil delta is very well known within the geological community; it was an enormous complex of streams that originated in

John Burroughs at Boyhood Rock. (Courtesy Frank Bergon)
Opposite: **Boyhood Rock and the Burroughs burial site. (Titus)**

the Acadian Mountains in what is now New England. From there these rivers flowed westward down into the Catskill Sea of today's New York State. Look at a good map of the Ganges Delta, which lies at the foot of the Himalayas, and you will see an excellent modern example of the old delta.

There was a problem, however, that bothered me at first. I was puzzled by the many small holes that littered the boulder's surface. At first I first guessed that they were fossil animal burrows. Could these be the burrows of Burroughs rock? Alas, the gods of nature writing would not be that kind to me. No, they just did not look right for burrows. Eventually, I found an especially well-preserved one and quickly recognized it as the cast of a fossil tree root. They were fossils of the Gilboa trees, from one of the world's oldest fossil forests. These were tropical plants, and so Boyhood Rock, a product of the Ice Age, must have had an older, equatorial ancestry.

Gilboa tree roots are common in the Catskills, but it was the first time I had ever seen them in a river sandstone. How could trees have been growing in the channel of a fossil river? In science, the solution of one problem often leads to another. A possible answer is that this stretch of the old channel had once been a great bend in the river. During an especially bad flood, the river carved a new

route and the old bend was abandoned, leaving a large, curved lake called an oxbow (see Thomas Cole's painting *The Oxbow*). The lake gradually filled with sediment, and then trees began to grow, their roots penetrating the old river sands. That's what we see today.

But there was another mystery that really bothered me. There are actually three boulders here. All match each other in terms of lithology and all have fossil tree roots. This can't be a coincidence, because the odds are too great; the three rocks must once have been joined. My guess is that there was once a much larger Boyhood Rock, transported not beneath a glacier but *within* it. As the ice melted, this boulder was lowered toward the ground. Stresses generated at this time caused the original rock to break up into the three pieces, each of which "landed" near the others and remains as we see them today.

And so it was that Boyhood Rock gave up its geological secrets. There is a great deal of satisfaction that comes from cracking a scientific problem, even if it is a problem of absolutely no practical significance. But all around me was a living natural history. A geologist is not likely to be able to enjoy the natural history here as John Burroughs once did. I am not a John Burroughs; I don't know much about the birds or the botany, but I thought that if I spent enough time at the rock, some of Nature's pleasures would come to me. They did, and I would soon find that Boyhood Rock was a living part of the Catskill landscape.

Evening, June 27th, 1996—This night is among the shortest of the year and you never can quite convince yourself that it is fully dark. After the sun sets, a faint glow lingers in the northwest. All night long, that glow traverses eastward across the northern horizon. Tonight, the sky is also lit by a nearly full moon. Perhaps because of all of this illumination, the faunas of Old Clump haven't truly settled down. Throughout the night there is the sound of chirping insects. A solitary bird is restless; off and on it chirps, warbles and twitters, a one-bird band anticipating the coming morn's avian chorus.

As the sky darkens, the late night pageant begins. The evening sky is ruled by the summer constellations—Scorpio, Sagittarius, and the Summer Triangle. But the nighttime sky is a fortune teller: an hour after midnight the great square of Pegasus appears and the sky foretells autumn. Before dawn the Pleiades prematurely announce winter's onset. Very late, Venus appears as a low bright light in the sky. An hour before the coming day a small cloud bank rolls in and the stars disappear. At last it is dark and the restless faunas of the forest finally go completely silent.

Before dawn, the clouds disappear and the horizon's glow swells in the northeastern sky and becomes a rising sun. As the first swelling of light occurs, a single sound emanates from the forest—"chirp"—After a long pause there is a second chirp and quickly a third. Soon a harmony of bird songs announces the impending day. There is something deliberate about this early morning singing—a distant rhythm to the songs that echo from the forest of Old Clump.

As Boyhood Rock gradually emerges from the darkness, there is little activity on the rock. A few ants wander about left and right of the Burroughs plaque. Near them, a tent caterpillar meanders very slowly. At the base of the rock, on its north end, a thin line of sluggish ants marches along. But mostly Nature is still asleep; in fact, there is a large spider, a "daddy long legs," sleeping soundly in a shallow grotto right on top of the rock.

The activities pick up as the sun rises and its light falls upon the rock's environs. A gentle breeze stirs and lifts a sweet, minty fragrance from the meadow below. The wind blows the sleeping spider's long legs around, but the arthropod resists awakening. Now the surrounding woods resound in a rising cacophony of chirps, calls, cries, caws, and warbles. A woodpecker begins a noisy breakfast deep within the forest while around the rock itself several hungry robins search for theirs. They are attracted by the good hunting on the mown lawn around the grave and in front of the rock.

By 5:40, the sun's light begins to come in sideways between the trees, and it falls upon Boyhood Rock. The rock starts to wake up. The ants around the plaque become more numerous and more active; they are wandering about more or less randomly. The tent caterpillar crawls away and a sow bug appears briefly. I watch the daddy long legs, but it sleeps on contentedly.

By 6:30 breakfast seems to be over for the birds, and their morning serenade begins to settle down. Over the next hour or so they seem to get even quieter. Replacing them are the first of the day's buzzing insects. These flit about in the meadow, and a few of them alight briefly upon the boulder. By 7:30 the rock's top becomes populated by a growing swarm of small flies. They are most distinctive with their tiger stripes and green and copper-colored heads. They make short flights about the rock, each one as much of a hop as it is a flight.

By 9:00 it appears that the day will be a fine one. The sky is clear and blue, the sun is shining brightly and the air is dry.

The photosynthetic foundations of the rock's ecosystem are easily seen now. There are four or more types of lichens cemented to the rock surface. On the shady north side there is an encrustation of moss. This is a primitive foliage, but it is well-adapted to its rocky habitat.

By 10:00 the sun rises above the trees and its light begins to fall upon the rock's eastern flank. The glow slowly advances across the front and top of the rock, and for the first time all of it basks in full sunlight. Cold-blooded animals like the warmth, and now they are becoming active. The lines of ants around the plaque march with a brisker pace. At exactly 10:37 I am fortunate enough to be watching as the daddy long legs awakens. Without so much as a stretch or a yawn it gallops off and disappears.

Some arachnid alarm clock must have just rung because within the next ten minutes I observe no less than five species of spiders upon the rock. One, a handsome, striped form, hops about actively, picking among the lichens. Does it eat lichens or does it feed upon prey within them? I cannot tell. There is an especially mean looking black spider; he watches me suspiciously with four ugly eyes and raises his fangs at me menacingly. Then there is a long-legged yellow-brown species of acrobatic spiders. Two of them hang on the edge of the rock and leap into the air. They are nature's bungee jumpers, hanging from their own silk threads. Do they leap for sport? I doubt it; I think they must be trying to ambush some flying prey.

At 11:00 the entire rock is sunlit and warm. The first human visitors appear, a family from Delhi. They have not been here for years and were passing by . . . Yes they have read Burroughs. But while the warm, sunny weather brings people out, it tends to slow nature down. It is siesta time at Boyhood Rock. All around the birds are growing quiet now and the tiger-striped flies have been driven away by the radiant heat that rises from the rock. But other insects are quite busy. The spiders are hopping around actively. I watch as two of them, one small and one large, fight for territory. The small one threatens with its fangs and the large one gestures back similarly. The two of them actively circle one another, each looking for an opening. This Lilliputian duel continues for quite some time before the predictable result; the large spider gains a momentary advantage and the small one flees in fear. It's a territorial triumph for the tiny bully, but a few minutes later it idles away to another location. Why all the fuss for such a short triumph? I do not know. All around me there must be thousands of such Darwinian dramas being played out in the temperate jungle of Old Clump.

For the next hour the rock bakes in a clear blue sky, and its little ecosystem slows down. Only an abundance of biting flies remains annoyingly active. But now the ants seem to have found something. A well-formed line of them stretches from the plaque to the right rear of the rock, and from there, off into the woods, I do not know how far. There are ants which are going and others who are coming from that unknown location. They follow a very narrow line and often collide head on. About a third of the returning ants carry a visible morsel of food. The rest? I don't know.

At about 1:00 a shadow begins crossing the rock. Nature's cycle is already swinging back toward darkness and by 2:30 the rock is once again completely in shadow. The spiders, having flourished in the sunlight, start to slow down again. The birds too, continue at their quietest, mostly emitting staccato snipping sounds amid a few real songs. The tiger-striped flies are back again, hopping about as before. I notice that sometimes one will hover in a low short semi-circle around another. The other usually disdainfully ignores the first or flies away. What drama is this? Is this insect love or more territorial wars? I do not know. The ants are emerging from several small grottos just left of the plaque. They are transporting their colony's eggs to behind the plaque. What is this mystery? Is the plaque now a good warm place for eggs to develop? It is not given to a geologist to understand such things.

Late afternoon approaches, and what breezes there were are slowing down and the larger flying insects come out. I see more moths and butterflies than before. The birds again seem to be more active. I hear a lot more singing than earlier in the afternoon. At 5:00 I am presented with still another mystery. The ants are bringing their eggs back from behind the plaque. They return them to those grottos and come out empty-handed and go back to the plaque. What strange purpose is this? What instincts do they follow?

As the afternoon shadow expands eastward from Boyhood Rock, it begins to cool down a bit. The sun is much lower in the sky now. Its light slants sideways and there is no glare. Because of this the colors of the valley before me are so much softer and richer. It's much more picturesque in late afternoon. At 5:45 more humans appear; a couple from town visits the rock. They weed the grave for a few moments, sit on the grave site wall and then depart. There is still much affection for the old writer who was buried here three quarters of a century ago.

By 7:00 the sun is sinking and most of the valley floor is falling into the shade. The shadow of Old Clump is moving across the valley, and soon it is starting to rise up the opposite slope. I can see the silhouette clearly now, and I watch in fascination as it climbs that distant slope, rising at an accelerating pace. It is quieter now, no breeze stirs at all and the birds have settled down once again. The line of ants is much thinner and they are moving more slowly.

I am hoping to see some precise signal of the oncoming darkness, but nothing happens. At 7:45 a single bird is warbling merrily. As it goes silent, the first cricket of the evening begins its song. Then the cricket goes silent. It is now as quiet as it has been all day, and for the first time, I can hear the gurgling of the spring above the rock.

All of the opposite mountain is in shade now, but the clouds are still bright in the day's last sunshine. I watch as the lower clouds slowly turn gray, and then, as the gray rises, even the highest clouds darken. It is the very shadow of the Earth that I am watching.

At 8:58 a solitary bird sings again, but only for a moment. The last of daylight fades quickly. In the distance I fancy that I can hear Brahms' Lullaby. The music is perfect for the time and for the place.

Kaatskill Life, Summer 1997

THIS "WOUNDEROUS PLACE"

IT'S SPRING, AND A YOUNG STREAM'S FANCY TURNS TO EROSION. All winter long snows have piled up, while ice has accumulated within the frozen ground awaiting the release brought by the returning warmth of the spring sun. Now the grounds are soft, and the waters are flowing into swollen and churning streams. This is the time to look for the spring torrents of Kaaterskill Clove.

The flow of most streams rises a great deal at this time of the year. Of course, not all streams are the same; they vary quite considerably. Geologists recognize a number of different types of streams, but I think that most of them can be classified into two of the most commonly observed categories: the mountain and the floodplain streams. As their names imply, these rivers have a lot to do with the landscapes that they flow through. However, it is not only activity, but time, which defines the streams.

Floodplain streams are the workhorses among rivers. They are usually large and heavily laden with sediment, mostly sand, silt and clay. It's their job to transport this material down the river to the ocean. Floodplain rivers are found in the lowlands, and they flow quietly across flat valley floors. Floodplain streams do have their moments of excitement, especially during the flood season, but most of the time they are stable and predictable.

Not so the mountain streams. They are not the large transporters of sediment. Narrow, but active, their job is to erode landscape, carving deep, jagged valleys into the highlands. We describe them with words such as "canyon," "gorge," "ravine," or "clove." These streams are far more erratic in their behavior than other streams. They are wildly active and energetic. Their white waters tumble down steep slopes. We use words like "torrent," "churning," and "swirling" to describe their flow. Mountain streams are noisy, foaming, and powerful. They have waterfalls, cascades, rapids, eddies, and cataracts. The young and reckless among us challenge them with canoes and kayaks; the rest of us watch from the safety of the banks. But all of us pause for a moment when we encounter one; they have majesty.

The finest mountain streams of the Catskills are those that form the cascades

Opposite: **The top of Kaaterskill Falls. (Titus)**

along the Wall of Manitou: the Catskill Front. One of them is Plattekill Creek, but it's hard to get close enough to this stream to really see it. The one to visit during a Catskill spring is Kaaterskill Creek, the most accessible of the mountain stream gorges. One should begin the trip upstream, and then follow an increasing swell of water down the canyon.

From the east or west, follow Route 23A to County Route 18 in the hamlet of Haines Falls. Turn east, on 18, heading toward the North/South Lake State Park. Watch for Laurel House Road and turn into it before getting to the park. Hike from the end of the road down the trail to the falls. Here Spruce Creek, an upstream tributary of Kaaterskill Clove, plunges over Kaaterskill Falls.

Depending on what kind of season it has been, there should be a good flow of water down the creek and over the falls. If you get there early enough in the season, there should still be a great cone of ice at the base of the upper falls. You can see the falls from the trail which winds its way above the falls along the north rim of the clove. This should only be followed with great care as the trail is likely to be wet and slippery at this season.

You may well have already been to this site, but if not, you do owe it to yourself to make the trip. For hundreds of years, people have been awestruck at this location. There is an inscription at the top of the falls, probably carved into the rocks by an early nineteenth-century visitor. It's now long-weathered and incomplete but it reads:

> *Wounderous pla . . . n rocks lofty & torne . . .*
> *r agin down the rudged steep*

I don't know who the carver of those words was, or when he was at the falls, but I do know the emotions he felt there.

The trail system in this vicinity is very old, having evolved from the paths and carriage roads of the hotel era, and it reaches all the best scenic overlooks. Maps are readily available. To see the other major falls of upper Kaaterskill Creek, hikers follow the Blue Trail east to the Layman Monument or, better yet, to Sunset Rock. From here there is a spectacular view of Haines Falls (not the village but the falls itself), at the head of the valley. The waterfall is distant and often hidden in shadow, but if the flow is high, it can be seen.

I like to visit Sunset Rock whenever I can. The view here changes considerably, and so I like to come at different times of the year and at different times of the day. In the morning, mists and fogs often enshroud the valley far below. I don't like high noon when too much of the sun's glare is reflected off the foliage and too much of the colors are lost in the harshness of the light. I much prefer mid-morning or late afternoon, when the light comes in at a low angle. The colors are rich and soft then, and best for viewing. In the summer, the view will be lush with the season's greenery. In winter it will be barren, and gray or white;

Opposite: Sunset Rock (Titus)

dark shadows of tree trunks will provide a sharp contrast with the white snow. Autumns here are breathtaking. Throughout the year, there is usually a haze as the air of the clove tends to be humid. But on those cool, dry days of spring, there is a clarity to the air that is unmatched during the rest of the year. Spring is a fine time to visit Sunset Rock.

Kaaterskill Clove has been a favorite of tourists and hikers since the early nineteenth century. This site also attracted many artists of the Hudson River School of Art, the first of which was Thomas Cole. The list goes on to include Sanford Robinson Gifford, Asher Brown Durand, William Henry Bartlett, Harry Fenn and many others. Even the political cartoonist Thomas Nast did some drawings here. A large number of our modern photographers have done work at these sites.

These actively eroding upper reaches of Kaaterskill Clove are typical of the mountain stream. The walls of the "rudged" valley tower above the stream. The primary erosional effort of the stream is to cut downward into the landscape. There is very little sideways erosion, and so the valley is narrow and has no flatland. This creates the picturesque scene that attracts us.

You can get a good intuitive sense of the greatness of geologic time on the Blue Trail of Kaaterskill Clove. The ages of the various facets of the landscape are well known. Look west at Haines Falls, the most youthful part of the landscape. It began to form after the Wisconsin Glaciation ended, freeing the clove from ice only about 14,000 years ago. Haines Falls has retreated up the valley a few hundred feet since that time. Kaaterskill Falls, which you cannot see from Sunset Rock, was similarly formed. There are other young features as well. Directly across the valley, several young canyons are cutting into the steep slopes of High Point Mountain, which towers above the south slope of the clove. There is less water in these streams, so they have not cut into the mountains as deeply as has Kaaterskill Creek at Haines Falls. While these three canyons are usually dry, they may be active at this time of the year. If so, look for cascades of white water plummeting down the slopes at extremely rapid rates of speed.

The great expanse of Kaaterskill Clove is much older than the small canyons at Haines and Kaaterskill Falls. Nevertheless, this is still a young valley and its steep walls, and narrow, white water streams are so typical of mountain streams. This canyon is associated with the last two great episodes of glaciation; that's young for geology. It's the first of these, the Illinoisan Glaciation, that began to scour the Wall of Manitou. After the glaciers melted away, erosion began to cut Kaaterskill Clove into the eastern front of the Catskill Mountains. All this was repeated during the next phase of the Ice Age, the Wisconsin Glaciation. The same story applies to Plattekill Clove as well.

Now look to the east where only a narrow glimpse of the Hudson Valley is

Opposite: Bastion Falls. (Titus)

Fawn's Leap. (Titus)

visible. One immediately sees that the Hudson has a far wider and deeper valley; it is orders of magnitude larger and older. The Hudson Valley was already very old long before Kaaterskill Clove began to form. It is at least tens of millions of years older. In this region, only the Berkshires to the east and the Catskills, themselves, are older than that. They were already very aged, long before the Hudson River Valley even began to form—hundreds of millions of years old.

Return to Route 23A and drive east into the Kaaterskill Clove. Park at the sharp bend in the road, and walk down to Bastion Falls. Downstream, the flow of water picks up, and Bastion Falls is likely to have a greater rush of white water than you saw above. Now some of the real strengths of the springtime stream should be apparent. There is power to the flow here. The now raging current breaks up upon the boulders and turns into the white froth of the cataracts below. The current splits into a chaos of competing cascades. There is noise at Bastion Falls but only a hint of what we shall hear farther downstream.

Below Bastion Falls the stream levels out for quite some distance. Subtly, Kaaterskill Creek is changing; water is seeping into the stream along its banks. It is on this stretch that the river gains its full volume and strength.

Farther down the gorge is Fawn's Leap, the lowest of the major falls. Here the stream gets to display all of its might at last. The surge of the spring stream will occur at some time in March or April. When I was at the falls in the spring of 1994, the flow was quite impressive. The steady roar and continuous foam of the falls makes it a great spring season spectacle. There are different ways to view the falls, and one should never be in a hurry. The sound, smell and feel of the falls are part of the experience at Fawn's Leap. I like to climb down low (but not too low) on the banks below the falls where I feel that I am part of the scene. There, the might of the falls is projected in its sound as well as in its sight, and there is a freshness in the fragrance of the passing waters that I much enjoy. On a breezy day there is also the feel of the water's fine spray on my face. Whenever possible, I enjoy climbing up onto the rocks above the falls and looking down upon the flow. Fawn's Leap is not a place just to be viewed, but a place to be savored with all the senses.

Geology is a contemplative science. Much of what the field has learned was produced by individuals who were long steeped in experience. Spend some time at Fawn's Leap, and you too may come to really experience the majesty of a mountain stream at this, its season of peak flow. Fawn's Leap can be thought of as a landscape machine. Look up at the walls of red sandstone towering above. These were carved by the same process of erosion which is happening within the falls today. It is this falls, and any number of its long gone predecessors, which have created Kaaterskill Clove. At Fawn's Leap you can come to truly appreciate the nature of the great chasm that has been cut at Kaaterskill Clove and the time that it took to carve it. This is landscape being formed as rapidly as it can be.

The spring torrent of Kaaterskill Clove is a must-see in the Catskills so wait for a particularly rainy spell of springtime weather and, a day or two later, do make the trip. A few words of caution are necessary. The spring torrents lure us too close to the edge. We are beguiled by their power and danger. The soils are loose and wet at this season, so please take great care when visiting this great vision. Too many of us have learned this lesson in the most bitterly painful way.

IN MEMORY OF HELEN ROBERTSON
Kaatskill Life, Spring 1995

THE HEART OF DARKNESS

THERE IS, if you can imagine it, a "darkest Catskills," a place where Nature still truly prevails. It is a wholly untamed wilderness where, even in our time, people are sometimes afraid to tread. Once you have entered it, it becomes a place that seems to draw you on but, no matter how deeply you go into it, and no matter how difficult your trek has become, it will only get worse. Still, it is a place that teases you on with promises of natural beauty that numb your normal cautions. It is a dangerous place, but, in the end, it is worth the risks; it is one of the most beautiful localities in all of our mountains, and that is saying a lot. But you always have to remember that one thing: no matter how difficult it is, it will only get worse. It is the canyon of Plattekill Clove.

You can never think about Plattekill Clove without comparing it to its big brother—Kaaterskill Clove. Each is a very large, deep ravine cut into the "Wall of Manitou": that great ledge we call the Catskill Front. Kaaterskill Clove is longer and deeper, and it is a rugged and majestic place. And Kaaterskill Clove also seems to be an older geological feature. It may well be more than 100,000 years old and, in that time, it has been able to carve a canyon bottom that rises relatively smoothly from the Hudson River lowlands to Haines Falls. Plattekill is shorter and not quite as deep but it is fundamentally different; here erosion has had time to create waterfalls but not the time to destroy them. This whitewater stream, as it descends its canyon, pauses at each sandstone ledge. Often it creates deceptively pretty little pools of water and then tumbles over the edge of the cliff to make a powerful waterfall. There is a geological irony here. The sandstone ledges that cap our modern falls are the lithified sediments of almost 400-million-year-

Upper Plattekill Clove on a misty morn. *Below*: **Plattekill Falls. (Titus)**

old Devonian age rivers. The sands of ancient rivers block the flow of modern creeks.

Thus it is that stratigraphy has given the Catskill Front a series of very rugged ledges, and at Plattekill, each one of them has its own waterfalls. Back at the older Kaaterskill Clove, the creek there has had time to erode its way through most of the ledges and only a few falls remain. Kaaterskill Clove is like a deep old wound that has had enough time to do some healing. Plattekill is more like a fresh stab. Both are rugged, both are beautiful, but Plattekill is more jagged and raw. Nature has done no healing in this canyon.

This is a wholly different clove, and it can only be seen from down below. It can be, quite literally, the heart of darkness. On an overcast day, as you ascend this canyon and the walls rise above you, it actually gets dark.

It once was a popular tourist attraction, and back in the late nineteenth century there were several hotels here. Many old postcards remain, but those times are long gone. Today, not many people hike the great canyon. It is a very rough place, and there are no marked trails; it is no place for the novice. And it is not a very easy place for the advanced hiker either. I, and some of the best hikers that I know, have actually confessed to have been intimidated by its reputation. But the canyon does beckon, and one August day four of us decided to give it a try.

The lower canyon is a deception; it seems to be there with the purpose of luring you on. It's picturesque but surprisingly easy to hike. The end of the last Ice Age gave this part of the clove a deep blanket of soft sediment, something we call an alluvial fan of sand and gravel. The post-ice age flow of water cut through those gravels and created a beautiful ravine. You can follow an easy unmarked trail along the rim of that ravine and gaze down into the jagged canyon below and enjoy the walk immensely. But remember, this is Plattekill; it will only get worse ahead.

As I said, there are many waterfalls in Plattekill; it's not easy to count them, but traditionally the number is 17. We reached our first and it was a beauty. Among the nicest things about the falls of Plattekill are the "plunge pools" that form beneath them. Over the millennia, high flows of water have tumbled over the falls and carved out deep pools at their bases. These form very fine swimming holes, which are real attractions. We found the messy evidence of much swimming and picnicking and general partying at the base of our first falls. But we had no time for any of these ourselves; we followed an easy trail up and over the falls and pushed on. Now we were really in the wilderness that makes up Plattekill Clove.

Soon I saw the first of many unusual boulders of the trek; it was large, five feet across, well weathered and nicely rounded. I looked it over carefully and found it to be a "foreigner." It was not composed of Catskill bluestone as it should have been. Instead it was a rock called gneiss. Gneiss is a metamorphic rock, which means it formed under very high temperatures and pressures; this one had formed in the Adirondacks or New England and it had been brought down the Hudson Valley and left here by the glaciers. Such rocks are called glacial erratics. I would look for, and find, quite a few other erratics during the rest of the day. They spoke to me of the ice age glacier that had preceded us here. Maybe fourteen thousand years ago a tongue of ice had climbed the clove, all the way to the top. It had carried those boulders with it and left them here when the climate warmed. Now those boulders were slowly traveling back down the clove. Plattekill tells a lot of stories when you look into its rocks. We pushed on.

At two hours into our ascent we passed a small tributary stream coming in from the right and then, very soon, another one on the left. These were what geologists call "parallel streams." They plunge down very steep slopes and are, all of them, nearly vertical; they are almost as much waterfalls as they are streams. Vertical streams are, of course, all parallel and hence the term. Our second one has had a number of names: it has been called "Black Chasm Creek," and "Coal Kiln Creek," and "Cold Kill Creek," and "Cross Clove Creek." The name doesn't matter much, but I would not soon forget this little stream.

On this day there was very little water in it, but there were a very large number of very big bluestone boulders. Steep parallel streams can transport such gigantic boulders with little difficulty; they get a large boost from gravity. For millennia, both of these streams had been funneling these great rocks out of the highlands above. Their journeys are not a very long, but they are very slow, and they will be tumbling down these canyons for many thousands of years to come. Plattekill is like some sort of reverse Sisyphus, it seems to be forever rolling rocks down the hill.

The idea that there can be streams of boulders was not new to me, but I was most impressed to see this one. We continued up the main canyon, and in a hundred yards or so, we encountered another stream of boulders, this one being in Plattekill Creek itself. There were hundreds of boulders, and many were more than ten feet across. I wondered how much they weighed. We had not much noticed it, but Plattekill had slowly become a steeper canyon. Its slope was great enough now so that it too was transporting the heavy weight of big boulders. I had seen Plattekill Clove as a fresh wound into the Catskill Front. Now the metaphor was working very well. My Catskill wound was now bleeding streams of boulders.

Next, we entered into what seemed like a whole new realm of Plattekill. Slowly, we found our attentions drawn upwards, as great vertical cliffs of sandstone came to tower above. And tower is just the right word; those walls were sheer cliffs—left and right—rising what seemed to be a hundred feet or more. At the same time, the canyon seemed to narrow and we found ourselves being funneled into a tighter squeeze. Here, we saw no more boulders, instead the cen-

Huge boulder in depths of Plattekill Clove. (Titus)
Opposite: **The dark, deep interior of Plattekill Clove. (Titus)**

turies of intense spring floods had flushed this part of the chasm clear. On this August day, the flow was very low, but the months of March and April must have witnessed a far more powerful flume of meltwater. I didn't like to think about the angry and icy gray flows of that season. There are some things that humans should not go and see, and this is one of them. We pushed on, clambering up the steep and often slippery bare red bedrock. The clouds rolled in high above and now the light in the deep canyon began to dim; we were truly in the heart of darkness.

But you must always remember: no matter how difficult Plattekill Clove is, it only gets worse. Now, after four hours of serious hiking, we found ourselves at the base of Green Falls, perhaps the tallest waterfalls of Plattekill Clove. Much to our dismay, these falls were a shear cliff and offered no hope of being climbed. The thought of turning back was even more dismaying. But, none of us had been here before, and it seemed that there was no way to go on. Only to our left, however, was there any glimmer of hope for completing our ascent; there we found the now-dry channel of another stream of boulders. It was either climb this or turn tail and retreat down the canyon. We began what would be an arduous ascent; it is a 270-foot upward climb over a chaos of rough, angular boulders. We made it, but it took quite a while and the reward was further disappointment. There at the top of our hard scramble was still another impediment.

Before us was another twenty-foot-thick ledge of sandstone, we had seen so many already on this day, but this one seemed to offer no way at all to pass up and over it. In Plattekill, it only gets worse. Once again, we faced the irony of being blocked by a nearly 400-million-year-old Devonian stream channel as we tried to ascend a modern creek. We explored to our left and to our right and found nothing but that vertical sandstone citadel. Now, it was getting late: should we climb all the way back down the Clove, a five-hour retreat that might carry us into darkness? Or should we press on in search of an escape route over this ledge? This was a difficult moment.

Well, all turned out; we explored farther to the right and found a dead tree lying against our ledge. It didn't have many branches left, but there were just enough to make an "Indian ladder" out of it. We pushed and pulled each other up the ladder and soon found a flat trail to the base of Plattekill Falls and the trail out of the upper clove. Our moods improved greatly.

Before breaking up, our little group climbed out to the overlook above the Devil's Kitchen, and there I saw the solution to the biggest mystery of the day. Why did Plattekill Clove persist in getting steeper and rougher as we climbed to its top? In an instant I saw the answer. At the Devil's Kitchen I saw that the sandstones here are broken by fractures of the sort that geologists call "joints." Joints are smooth, flat, vertical fractures of the rocks. They are like faults, except that there has been no motion of the rocks on either side. Here, as is always the case, the joints are closely spaced and, those of Plattekill Clove, cross the clove along a northeast to southwest compass direction. That means that as large masses of rock break loose and fall, they leave tall vertical walls that loom above the head of the clove. The fracturing was concentrated in the upper reaches of the clove, and this had accounted for the ever-increasing steepness. The broken joints had also, no doubt, provided the bulk of the boulders that I had been seeing all day long. It will, no doubt, provide many more boulders for millennia to come. Our conquest was now complete; not only had we climbed Plattekill Clove, but also we had solved one of its best geologic mysteries.

After our long and strenuous day, my companions were happy to disperse and return to their homes. I, however, had a special privilege: the Catskill Center for Conservation and Development had loaned me their little red cabin for the night. That's the one at the top of Plattekill Falls. I would spend a very nice evening on its porch listening to the roar of the water passing into the great clove that was now, happily, beneath me.

Late in the evening, more clouds rolled in, and all around me it became very dark. The air was still and the summer insects were very loud. From high up above, on Plattekill Mountain, came the cry of a single coyote. It was quickly joined by the howls of a whole pack of them. I am told that they do this after making a kill.

This is a wild place.

Kaatskill Life, Fall 2004

The little red cabin at the top of Plattekill Clove. (Titus)

GREAT RIVERS IN THE SKY

L ANDSCAPES are the products of millions and sometimes hundreds of millions of years of slow development. They reflect the many processes of weathering, erosion, climate change and biology that have been working upon them for all those lengths of time. Not surprisingly, there are often real mysteries hidden in the landscapes. We find features that puzzle us: what are they? How did they form? Our Catskill landscapes are among the most beautiful anywhere, but when you learn to look beneath the surface there are wonderful mysteries here to puzzle over. The science that does this is called geomorphology. In traveling through the western Catskills, I came across one of those wonderful puzzles.

Way out in the western Catskills, several of our larger streams display some very odd patterns of flow. They loop back and forth through large sinuous meanders. My particular favorite location is at Shinhopple. There the East Branch of the Delaware River flows through a rather deep canyon as it meanders north and south through great lazy loops. Nearby, the West Branch of the Delaware does much the same. Between Walton and Deposit, the West Branch passes through a number of similar loops. Here, however, the drama of the effect is largely lost as much of the canyon has been flooded by the Cannonsville Reservoir. The loops and the deep canyons are all there, but they are mostly submerged. And it is not just the two branches of the Delaware that display this peculiar landscape. The combined flow of the two, at least from Hancock to Narrowsburg, does much the same.

These are lovely stretches of the rivers. Take State Route 30 southwest from Margaretville, or State Route 10 southwest from Walton to see the branches. Or take Pennsylvania Route 191 to see the trunk stream. It's all pretty much the same: heavily forested hills crowd the river banks. Their slopes rise steeply to hilltops, high above. On one of those clear, high-pressure-system days in the late summer, with a noontime sun shining straight down into the valley, the effect is wonderful. The rich green of the trees and the blue sky frame the sparkling waters below. In late summer the flow of water is low and there are complexes of sand bars visible as well.

The narrow valleys seem to work to confine, or even imprison, the pretty rivers flowing back and forth across what seem to be all too narrow floodplains.

Opposite: **Large sinuous meanders on the East Branch of the Delaware River. (Courtesy, New York State Museum)**

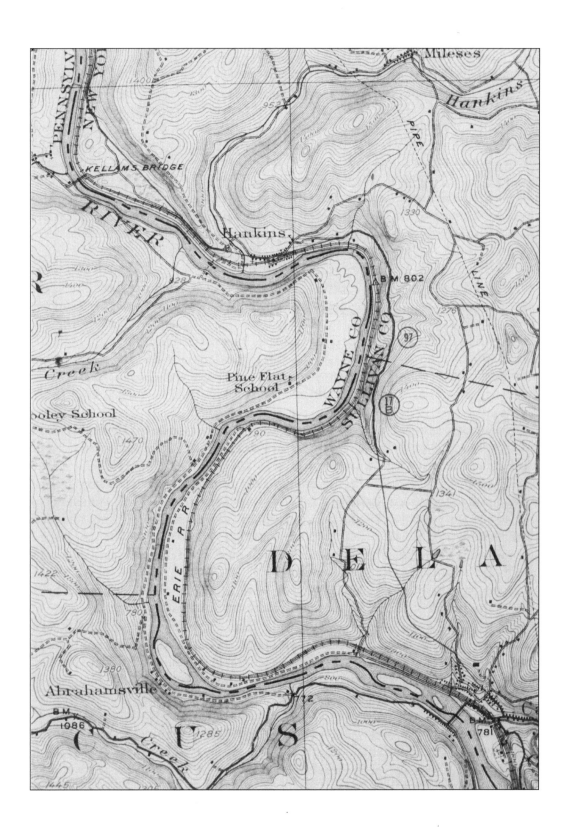

That's one more of the oddities we see in this region. There are meanders within meanders; the rivers flow back and forth through valleys that, themselves, meander back and forth. What on earth is going on here?

The key to all this is an understanding of the river meander, one of Nature's most graceful landscape features. If you would like to go and see a good one, travel to Vromans Nose, near Middleburgh and climb up to the top. From the eastern edge of the hilltop you can look down into the valley and see a very fine meander loop. Schoharie Creek has carved a great, wide, lazy loop here. Though there is only a single meander, it is a very good one, and there is a lot to learn from it. On the outside of the curve the river is thrown up against its own bank. On the quieter inside of the loop there is an accumulation of sand, a sandbar with a beach of sorts.

The meander loop is the product of the river's own physics. As it rounds a bend, the currents are thrown outward and they erode a widening loop. The eroded sands have to end up deposited somewhere nearby and that is on the inside of the loop. So a normal loop ends up with two sides, a steep eroded outside and the sandy beach on the inside. Good meander loops are typical of large river floodplains. The river tends to meander back and forth across the floodplain, finding it easy to sculpt the sands and gravels into the expected loops. At Vromans Nose, Schoharie Creek has a fine sandy floodplain so the loop we see there is perfectly normal.

And the meander *loops* we see on the narrow floodplains of the Delaware are perfectly normal as well. But that leaves a very big question left unanswered. How did those very large meanders of the Delaware valleys come to be? It's easy to understand how a river could erode its own looping channel, but how does a *valley* come to form meanders? Bedrock erosion does not follow the same laws of physics as the erosion of sand and gravel. So how is it that we get the same results? How is it possible that meanders, which should be cut into sands and gravels, are cut into bedrock? It seems to be a tough question and that's the problem in the western Catskills.

The answer to that key question gets us back to the first thing that I said: landscapes are the products of millions of years of history. River landscapes, like all others, wear the scars of their pasts and it's important to know that rivers have had many pasts. By that I mean that river landscapes have passed through many chapters in their histories. There were times of dry climate with little flow of water and times of wet climate with high flow. There were times when a river landscape may have dropped below sea level and the river would have submerged and times when it was elevated far higher than today. If we wonder how these great valley meanders came to be, we must think in terms such as this.

Geologists began understanding all this in the late-eighteenth century and a century later they were able to use their understanding to begin to formulate

Steep slopes of the Delaware River. (Titus)

answers to problems like those of the valley meanders. By the early twentieth century, geologists were taking the problem apart to see if they could come up with some answers. River meanders, they reasoned, only form on floodplains so maybe there was a time when the western Catskills had eroded into a broad flat floodplain. It would be normal to expect that an ancestral Delaware River would form nice meander loops upon that ancient floodplain. That solved part of the problem, but what about the rest?

The second part of the problem was to figure out how such ancient meanders could have cut into the bedrock landscapes of today. The answer was to imagine that there had been a prolonged period of regional uplift. If the crust rose hundreds of feet upwards then, at the same time, rivers would have to carve hundreds of feet downward into those rising rocks. But that created a problem: the old rivers were trapped in their old meandering channels. The result was that downward erosion would preserve the old meander as it cut into bedrock. With time the valley walls would evolve into steep slopes with picturesque rivers rounding the great curves of the old meanders. That's, of course, just what we have.

If all this is true, then the great loops in the Delaware are real marvels of nature. In effect, they are fossil meander loops, preserving ghost images of the Delaware as it had been long ago.

But that causes us to ask just exactly where and when did these fossil rivers exist: the answers are more marvels of nature. The "where" part of the question takes you way up into the sky. Gaze upwards far above today's rivers. These ancient streams were at least hundreds and possibly a few thousand feet up in what is today's sky. Astonishing, yes, but it makes perfect sense. All landscape surfaces have been greatly lowered by weathering and erosion for millions or even hundreds of millions of years. Thus, long ago, they must have been "up there." If you visit any of these western Catskill rivers, gaze up and try to imagine a meandering ribbon of water, exactly parallel to today's stream, but way up in the sky.

When did these rivers in the sky exist? We're not certain and must make guesses, but many geologist believe that these rivers may date back to the late Mesozoic time, about 140 million years ago. Back then these were just meandering streams winding back and forth across a broad, flat, sandy floodplain that made up much of the region. Then a great crustal up-warping began that affected most of eastern North America, and this is the event that resulted in these entrenched meanders.

What were these rivers like back then? I can only make an educated guess. But we do know a great deal about the climate and the biology of the late Mesozoic. This was a very warm period in earth history, the climate was certainly tropical and banks of our ancient rivers would have thus teemed with life. Dense jungles must have lined the river bank. Back, away from the river bank, those jungles would have been populated mostly by conifers. Along the banks, however, a very important biological event was occurring. The flowering plants had only recently evolved, and some of the world's earliest populations of such plants were growing along our Catskill river banks. These included many familiar types of trees, early types of oaks, maples and especially sycamores.

All of these are rather familiar, even ho-hum looking plants, found in any of our forests today. But the animals were different, and that's where the really exciting part of my story begins. Those jungles certainly had diverse populations of dinosaurs living within them. It's quite likely that there were duck-bill dinosaurs along with the horned Triceratops. This landscape was a dangerous place, and Tyrannosaurs probably stalked the jungle along with other scary predators. Pterodactyls, less dangerous but equally impressive, flew overhead. The waters of the rivers themselves teamed with ancient fish and great fifty-foot-long crocodiles.

These are the oldest stretches of river that I know of anywhere, and that is incredible. If you are a Catskill fisherman and occasionally stand on the banks of any of the Delaware River basin streams, remember that dinosaurs once stood where you stand and drank from the water that are passing before you. It is a wonderful "Jurassic Park" view of the western Catskills.

Is all this true? Well, there is not a single bit of hard evidence for any of this. Those ancient rivers flowed south into what is today Chesapeake Bay, eroding away all of their own landscapes. They carried off all of the rock and sediment that once covered the region. It may be that hundreds and even thousand of feet of landscape are now gone along with all the earthly remains of those dinosaurs and forests. The proof has eroded!

So how could I tell my story? Such scientific accounts are deductions based on a broad understanding of earth history derived from studies elsewhere around North America and, indeed, the entire globe. I do not know of a better explanation, nor have I even heard another one, for these bends in the rivers. No matter how you explain them, the great meanders are scenic wonders. Whether they are small meanders on narrow floodplains or great majestic bends in the largest of valleys, they add so much to the landscape beauty. These streams are well known for their good fishing, and although many of our local fishermen already knew they were in Heaven, few knew they had gone to the "great rivers in the sky."

Kaatskill Life, Spring 2000

MIDNIGHT ON THE RIVER STYX

CAN YOU CELEBRATE A MILLENNIUM IN A PLACE WITHOUT TIME? I would find out. The opportunity came with a big event at Howe Caverns: a millennium eve party underground. I couldn't resist; Howe Caverns is not just a cave, it is an underground stream, called the River Styx. It was the perfect setting for a geologist to spend a New Year's Eve. But, I had those doubts. It seemed to me that a cave would be the least likely place to observe a great landmark in time; after all, a cave is so separated from the rest of the world. Down there, the days, the moons, and the seasons pass without note. How could one observe a millennium so removed from the normal cues of time?

Our party began above ground with dinner, music, and dancing. Our gaiety, at the close of the twentieth century, had not been matched at the century's dawn. My mind drifted back those one hundred years. Back then, the cave had hit upon hard times and had closed down. The cave had been a big success from its opening in 1843, but it must have been quiet and dark on the millennial night of 1899. There are some vestiges of the nineteenth century still here. The old Lester Howe Hotel still stands but only as a derelict reminder of a one-time splendor. Beside

The New Year's Eve party. (Titus)

the hotel is the cave's old tourist entrance, now all boarded up. It doesn't matter, nobody will try to get in; that part of the cave was destroyed by quarry operations during the early twentieth century. Much of the original tourist cave, as Lester Howe knew it, has been lost.

These were somber thoughts about a somber New Year's Eve, but this time we would do much better. The best part of the night would be spent underground. Our descent into the cave, at 10:30, was by elevator, a mid-nineteenth-century device that had restored the Howe Caverns to success in 1929. A minute's ride brought us 160 feet beneath the surface. The elevator door opened, and we entered a chamber called the "Vestibule." Of course, I immediately noticed the limestones that made up the walls. I was especially interested in the strata near the floor. They are parts of what is called the Manlius Limestone, a thinly laminated sequence of very fine grained rock. Gray and black in color, these layers were hardly likely to catch the attention of the average tourist. But I was more geologist than tourist; my finger reached out and gently touched one of the lighter laminations.

I was touching a moment in time, and this stratum transported me to another great millennium of history. For me, it had become the Devonian time period, the evening of December 31st, 399,998,001 BC. In a few hours it would be exactly 400 million years ago. This was not just the turn of a millennium, but something humans do not have a word for. I had gone 400,000 millennia into the past, millions of centuries had passed in reverse. I was no longer in a cave, I was outside on a warm night. Gentle humid breezes passed across my face. In the pre-mid-

The fine grained Manlius Limestone. (Titus)

Behind the "Bridal Altar." (Titus)

night darkness I saw another, very ancient, River Styx. This was a river of salt water, flowing eastward in front of me. This River Styx was a tidal channel on an enormously broad tidal flat. All around me for miles was the tropical land of the Manlius Limestone, a vastness of tidal flats. Scores of similar channels carried water across it, all reflecting a large moon. But now the tide was rising rapidly, and a flood of water, dirty with sediment, overflowed the channel and quickly submerged the flats. The endless ebb and flow of the tide is an emblem of time, but this particular cycle was special. Soon the flood tide reached its crest, and the rush of water stilled just as the new millennium turned. At this turn of the tide, a thin layer of silt and clay settled upon that flat. I reached into the shallow water and touched that layer of silt, and then I was back in the cave, touching a cold wall of rock.

We wandered onward, down into the cavern itself. We passed the "Rocky Mountains" and then the great "Gallery of Titan's Temple." We came to something called the "Bridal Altar," which was at the top of a staircase. Marriages have been performed here throughout the cave's history. I took a look into a grotto behind the altar. This small chamber is a part of the original route of the River Styx; it leads down the oldest part of the cave. Long ago, this route became clogged with mud and abandoned. Turning back I looked up and found a beautifully curved ceiling. It was the ceiling of the old route, scoured into a smooth surface by the ancient flow of water. Now I found myself once again in the deep past; it was the midnight of Dec. 31, 5,998,001 BC. I was in a very low, narrow

The derelict Lester Howe Hotel. (Titus)

Howe Caverns in the midst of a strong current of rushing water. This was the River Styx as it had first been, six thousand millennia ago, more of a tunnel than a cave. This rush of water, powerful as it might be, was just the humble beginning of the now complex cave system. That River Styx rushed off past the Bridal Alter and down the old passage. It swept me along with it on an *Alice in Wonderland* journey.

The flow was powerful and agitated, and my ride was a rough one. I traveled what seemed a long distance along the tunnel, and then I was carried downwards and dumped unceremoniously upon a dark river bank. Time had played a trick on me; now it was midnight, December 31st, of the year 999 AD. I was in the stretch of the cave that once existed downstream and beyond today's tourist cave. I was in a chamber called "The Chapel." That was strangely fitting as there was, next to me, the skeleton of a ten-year-old Indian boy. This lonely little boy would observe the turning of the millennium silently. No one was looking for him, nobody missed him, nobody mourned his loss. His family had suffered all of those torments, but that had been centuries earlier, and now no one remembered his disappearance. Even his tribe, an Algonquian culture, was now long gone from the Cobleskill vicinity; in 999 AD it was the Owasco Iroquois who lived here instead, and that was mostly only in the summers. His skeleton was a fine one, except for the one badly broken ankle. Many centuries later, when the next human, Lester Howe, would finally pass by, those bones would be long gone. Today even his "Chapel" is lost, having fallen victim to the quarry operation that consumed so much of Lester Howe's cave.

Above and outside the cave it was now the year 1000; the first midnight of the second millennium would find a gibbous moon above the Cobleskill region. Its rays shone down upon a dark, snowless landscape. It was a warm winter, and no snow had yet fallen. Here and there, especially near the creek, there were the remains of summer Iroquois Indian encampments and leftover bean fields. The recent growing season had been a good one, but the Indians were now gone. They were in their winter camp, near Vromans Nose in the Schoharie Creek Valley. The Iroquois didn't celebrate the millennium, they did not know of such things, but they did have better causes for celebration on this night. The warm climate and ample crops had made this a good winter, and that was more important than any calendar event.

I left that New Year's Eve and found my way up the Cavern to Lake Venus. This was a younger passage than the one I had just traveled. The River Styx had originally carved the Bridal Altar tunnel but later abandoned it and carved a newer passage into the floor of the old one. This younger part of the cave is narrower than the older and higher reaches. Nature has dammed this part of the cave and made it a lake. Now the boatman of the River Styx was taking New Year's revelers on a boat ride across the lake.

I continued up the Cave and rejoined several celebrants at the Gallery of Titan's Temple. The chamber has a high ceiling, and the River Styx makes a rapid descent from that old upper level to the newer lower one. Titan's Temple is fes-

The boat ride. (Titus)

tooned, like so many places in the cave, with picturesque stalactites. They hang from the ceiling like icicles. And, indeed, once there had been real icicles here as well. In my imagination I traveled back twenty millennia to Howe Caverns at the peak of the Ice Age: now I was celebrating the New Year's Eve of December 31st, 18,001 BC.

New Year's Eve is supposed to be cold, but this one was something else. The cave temperature was 11 degrees, which was the average annual temperature above. Up there, the Cobleskill vicinity lay beneath 4,000 feet of ice, under the huge Laurentide Glacier, which stretched southward to New Jersey. The River Styx was, of course, now a river of ice, it had been for centuries. Its final flow had frozen like a waterfall in winter. I gazed at the sinuous patterns of the ice; it looked like an ice-sculpture of a flowing river. I flashed an imaginary flashlight back and forth through enormous stalactites of ice that hung from the ceiling and reached the floor of the cave. The colors were magnificent, but it was a very cold and very creepy cave to be in. Caves are, by their very nature, spooky places, but at this moment Howe Cavern was probably more isolated and more spooky than it ever has been or that it ever will be again. The incredible silence made it all the worse. My image and my discomfort were, however, fleeting. After all, only my imagination was actually in this ancient cave, it was really New Year's of 1999, and I belonged to the present.

Midnight at last approached and the whole party gathered in a chamber above Lake Venus. We cheerfully counted down the last moments of 1999 and toasted the approach of the new millennium. But I could not escape the past. In a grotto behind us was another wonderful image from the Ice Age, and the New Year's Eve of 12,001 BC. There, I saw thickly stratified layers of gray silt and clay. It was an ice age deposit. If we had been here 14 millennia earlier we would have found that Howe Caverns was completely submerged beneath the icy waters of glacial Lake Schoharie. The Ice Age, at that time, was coming to an end. Those 4,000 feet of ice that had been above were now melted away, but great glaciers still blocked and dammed the Mohawk and Schoharie Valley drainage systems. An enormous lake flooded much of the region and the entire cave.

There was still a River Styx of sorts, but it was just a strong current flowing through the cave. And it was a dirty current, cloudy with silt and clay. Every few moments puffs of sediment swirled and wafted along. In the summer, the sediment was light colored and coarse while in the winter the currents slowed down and darker and finer grained sediments were deposited. These had pretty much filled the cave to a thickness of ten feet or so. After the Ice Age was completely over and all of the Mohawk and Schoharie glaciers melted away, all this lake water drained out of the cave. The flow of the River Styx resumed for real, and it eroded into the mud creating the exposure I was looking at.

Some of us headed back up the cavern. I found better ice age strata behind a fallen stalactite called Tom Sawyer's cap. We continued and soon got to an enormous heap of boulders called the "Rocky Mountains." I realized that I was looking at the most feared danger of a cave; these great boulders had fallen from the ceiling; they represented an ancient cave-in. I looked up at the ceiling here, and in my imagination, I heard a great cracking sound and saw those boulders crash down with an immense roar. The air was filled with dust and a clattering rain of gravel followed for a few moments. I did not find any of this very alarming, however, there was nothing to fear here. You see, my visions of the Ice Age led me to suspect that this cave-in had occurred soon after the lake waters had vacated the caverns, perhaps 13,000 years ago. With the cave roof weakened by all the weight that had been placed upon it and with the buoyancy of the lake waters gone, this cave-in had been inevitable. But that was then and this is now; cave-ins are extremely rare events.

The evening was late and we were heading back now. Our wanderings led us into one of the most remarkable stretches of the cave, the "Winding Way." The narrow and very deep gash in the limestone was, without doubt, the product of rushing waters, an old tributary of the River Styx. Looking upwards, I saw another smoothly scoured ceiling. That recorded the earliest stages of flow, back when the Winding Way was just a small tunnel. Since then, the currents had cut downwards to create this narrow, curvy cavern. It is dry now but I thought that in the past, especially right after the Ice Age, there must have been quite a flow here.

However, I was soon distracted from this vision. I looked at the wall of rock carefully and began to find fossils. There were fossil snails and other shellfish. Then there were coral-like creatures as well. I soon found nautiloids, ancient ancestors of the squid. All of these were exposed, in cross section, on those vertical walls. My view got a lot better, farther along, as we continued back nearly to the Vestibule. My geologist's eyes had looked into the rocks, and I was beginning to see still another vision from the distant past. We had walked right into the midst of an ancient fossil reef.

Once again, I had returned to the Devonian time, a New Year's Eve of maybe 395,000,000 years ago. This was the Coeymans Limestone, and it is above and different from the Manlius. This was not a tidal flat, it was a shallow marine seafloor, rich in plant and animal life. The best of it was the reef. There are no more fascinating seafloors than those of today's coral reefs. But this was a Devonian reef, and it was not composed of corals. This reef was made up of a coral-like animal known to science as the stromatoporoid. They are long extinct, but once they had been the most abundant creatures of the Howe Caverns site.

Reef animals, like humans, like to have parties at midnight; they become most active in the darkness. But those Devonian parties were long over and our time was now short, too. Our party and our trip through the cave, like the old millen-

***Opposite*: The "Winding Way." (Titus)**

nium, had reached its end. We quietly rode the elevator upwards to the surface. My fears that I would have been out of touch with time had evaporated. Howe Caverns may not see the passage of the days and seasons, but it has witnessed the passage of hundreds of millions of years, and it wears the scars of all that time. I had, on this night, not just passed through one milestone in history, but very many.

Kaatskill Life, Spring 2000

THE ABYSS

EVERY YEAR, tens of thousands, maybe hundreds of thousands of people, come to visit the Catskills. Most are attracted by the scenery, and the rocks have a lot to do with the making of those picturesque landscapes. But is it possible some of the rocks themselves are visitors to the Catskill region? Can rocks move and, if so, could some of them have come here from lands far away? Well the answer to those seemingly preposterous questions is a surprising *yes*. And, of course, that's not all; in science the answer to one question usually leads to many others. There are subjects here very much worth investigating.

I began pondering these questions recently when I received a reader's letter asking about one of the region's best-known rock exposures. It is the dinosaur skin outcrop in New Baltimore, along Route 9W, about a mile north of the Thruway entrance. "Dinosaur skin," did I really say that? Before this article gets completely out of hand, I had better do some very quick explaining. The outcrop I just described displays some rather eye-catching sedimentary structures and the story goes something like this: Long ago, these rocks impressed a local high school science teacher. He imagined he was looking at the fossil of a dinosaur and urged people to go and visit it. I don't know how, but professional geologists picked up the story, and it soon seeped into the geological folklore of the outcrop. Since then, all geologists, visiting the site, have been calling it the "dinosaur skin." We know better than that, but as I said, it is now folklore. At any rate this really is one of the most interesting geological sites around here, and even without a genuine dinosaur, it has probably been visited by most of the geologists of the Northeast.

The New Baltimore outcrop is part of what is called the Normanskill

The "dinosaur skin." (Titus)

Formation. That's a unit of rock that makes up much of the middle Hudson Valley. The Normanskill takes us back almost half a billion years, to a time when our region was very, very different. Off to the west, in what is now central and western New York State, there was a shallow tropical sea much like the Bahamas of today. Clear, aqua-colored waters covered a seafloor rich in primitive marine shellfish. Off to the east, that seafloor deepened steeply. Out there, the water was dark and cold. In the far distance there, volcanoes were rising and breaking the surface of the water. These were the beginnings of a volcanic island archipelago. With time, a large volcanic landmass would rise out of the sea and loom over the horizon much as Indonesia and New Guinea do today in the Pacific. This would evolve into a moderately large mountain range, which was soon to begin a major uplift. But as these mountains, called the Taconics, began to rise they would actual begin to be thrust westward and press against North America. This would cause problems.

There had been a long, deep, north/south–oriented ocean basin that covered much of today's western Massachusetts. As the ancient volcanic archipelago pressed westward, that sea was squeezed; as a result it narrowed and deepened. Such basins today are called trenches, and they make up the deepest parts of the Earth's oceans. The most famous, the Marianas Trench, is more than seven miles

View of Olana. (Titus)

in depth. Ours was probably not so deep, but back then, our area's rocks were forming at the bottom of very great abyss!

The oldest rocks of this abyss are not seen in New Baltimore. There is a much better place to see the Normanskill Formation, and that is at the estate of Frederic Church's Persian Revival mansion "Olana," on the eastern side of the Hudson. As you cross the Rip Van Winkle Bridge from the west, you will see Mount Merino to the north. It is largely composed of bedded chert, a type of rock you probably know as flint. You can see a good exposure of that rock if you head south on the highway and approach Olana. On the left (east) side of the road, just short of the Olana entrance, you will see an excellent outcrop of the Mount Merino Member. That's the name of this, the lower and older member of the Normanskill.

When Frederic Church was planning his home in the 1860s, he wanted a fine building stone. He was incredibly lucky and found it right there on his own property. The Mount Merino makes up much of Quarry Hill, just south of Olana. Church didn't use the chert, it was probably too brittle, but he seems to have found a very good horizon of fine-grained sandstone in a series of small quarries that are still just barely visible on Quarry Hill.

But most of the Olana landscape is made up of bedded chert, and chert is a very fascinating variety of rock. It conjures up images of the great deep marine trench that was once here. Dark, cold and completely silent, such a seafloor would have had few, if any, living creatures on it. But that was not the case up above in the shallow, sunlit surface waters. There such oceans are often teeming with life. In this case, teeming with single-celled organisms, protozoa we call radiolarians. Radiolarians are remarkable among protozoa in that they have an ability to extract silica from seawater, and they use it to create wonderful tiny skeletons. These display a remarkable array of geometric forms. After death, their "shells" accumulated on the sea bottom in thicknesses of sediment called siliceous oozes. With time this skeletal ooze hardened into the bedded chert I have been talking about. That's the origin of the Mount Merino Member of the Normanskill and, to some extent, that's the origin of Olana. The old ocean must have produced enormous, truly astronomical, numbers of radiolarians because they have produced hundreds of feet of bedded chert.

But this is not the end of the story. There is a second, younger horizon of the Normanskill Formation, called the Austin Glen Member. Back then, in the Ordovician time period of about 450 million years ago, the crust here was very unstable. Today, we think of places like California when we ponder unstable landscapes, but back then it was our turn here in New York State. As that volcanic archipelago was being uplifted into the Taconic Mountains, there were some very great stresses generated. As I said, much of this great landscape was also being thrust westward. It will likely amaze you to learn that the rocks of the Normanskill have traveled about 75 miles westward to their present location.

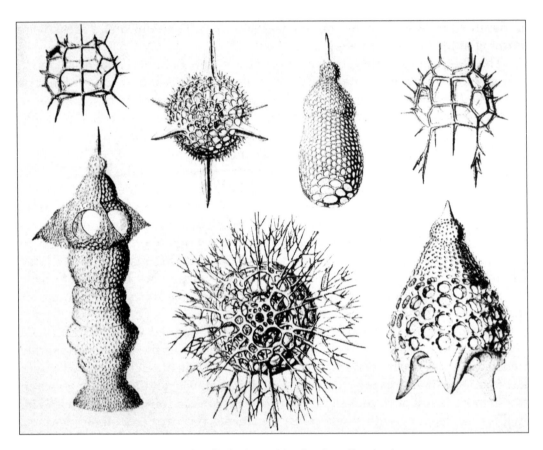

Typical radiolarians. (Author's collection)

They formed somewhere in the western Massachusetts and were shoved our way by much the same crustal forces that uplifted them.

Back then, the Hudson-Catskill area must have been periodically wrenched with earthquakes, and often very great ones, as the thrusting and uplift continued. You can see some of the deformation yourself. The strata found here were once nearly horizontal, but during mountain building and thrusting, they came to be tilted into their present nearly vertical inclination. Imagine, for a moment, how much energy was expended in tilting the heavy crust this much. Mountain-building events of this sort are serious business!

But it is that deep oceanic trench that is the center of our attention right now. It is the fate of mountains that they should crumble almost as fast as they are uplifted. Those rising and quaking Taconic Mountains were rapidly weathering and eroding away so there was a lot of sediment pouring into our trench. The steep slopes of the trench made the sediment unstable, and periodically, large masses of sand would tumble down into the deep. These were submarine avalanches which geologists call turbidity currents. That's where we get to the dinosaur skin.

If you visit the New Baltimore site, you will find two types of rock. One is very dark, even black, very thinly laminated rock called shale. That was once the mud on the bottom of the old seafloor. Mud was the normal deposit on the deep ocean basin. The other rock type is thickly bedded sandstone, and it was those layers of sandstone that formed from our turbidity currents.

If you do go there, look at the surface I have illustrated. There is a distinct lobate structure on the rocks of the exposure; the lobes are called flute casts. They were produced by those submarine avalanches. As the avalanche sands tumbled down slope, they picked up speed and may have reached thirty miles per hour. The sands pressed into the soft underlying mud and produced those lobate structures. There must have been more; there is a rhythmic wave-like pattern to the lobes at New Baltimore. Geologists have puzzled over this and guessed that there was a "harmonic pattern" to the avalanching.

Some other interesting structures that caught their attention were called drag marks. Somewhere along the line, the currents had dragged objects (who knows what?) down the slope. As they were pulled along, they left long prints in the sediment. All of this eventually hardened into rock. There are several very fine drag marks at the New Baltimore location, and geologists have debated exactly when and how they had formed.

All in all, New Baltimore offers geologists a pleasant time spent at a fine out-

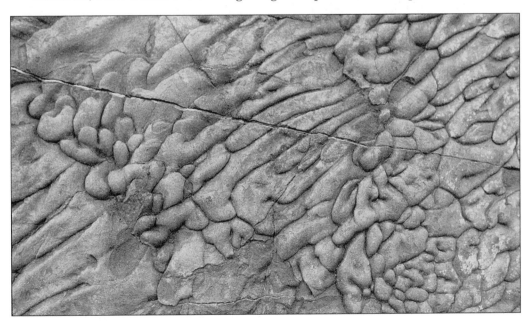

Close up view of flutes casts. (Titus)

crop. It is a genuine geological "tourist trap," and anybody who is anybody in Northeastern geology has been there. There is much to learn at such tourist traps; they are windows into the past.

But the real tourist attraction in the area is Olana itself. I stood on the bank in front of the south-facing porch of the old mansion and gazed at its fine view of the Hudson Valley and Catskill Mountains. This is one of the great vantage points

View of Hudson Valley from Olana, with thenCatskills in distance. (Titus)

from which to see the Catskills. There are days when the atmospheric conditions are just right and the mountains seem to reach out to you. It's not just a view; this is also a genuine work of art. Frederic Church intended that the porch should have this vista; it is, among many others, one of his "planned views." For thirty years he was able to enjoy the scene, and I envy him that.

But as a geologist, I am privileged to see some other views at Olana. On that wonderful site my mind drifted back into deep time. I was at the bottom of the abyss that was once here. The waters were cold and black, but more than anything else they were still and silent. This was a dead seafloor. Nothing crawled across the mud and nothing swam in the waters. I scooped up some of the mud; it was soft and sticky. It was foul with the remains of dead microbes that constantly rained in from above.

With time the avalanches came. The stillness was abruptly interrupted as the seafloor was jolted by seismic shocks. Shortly thereafter great masses of sediment began tumbling down the slopes. For long minutes there was the rush of dirty water. The torrent boiled as murky clouds billowed upwards all around me. Then the current slowed and gradually the water cleared. The Olana seafloor returned to its silent, dead stillness.

My mind's eye rose through tens of thousand of feet of quiet water until it reached the surface of the sea. I gazed eastward and saw dense black clouds rising above the horizon. The blackness drifted my way, and soon it rained volcanic dust into the water all around. Then I looked back eastward again and now a rising landmass had replaced the volcanic clouds on the horizon. The stark profile of volcanoes defined this new horizon

The passage of time accelerated. As I watched, this landmass grew taller and its shores swelled out toward me. I was soon lifted out of the sea by the rising gray crust. Occasionally, the earth beneath me shook with powerful quakes as the land rose higher and higher. Eventually, I found my imaginary self high atop a still rising Taconic Mountain range. To the north and south, volcanoes erupted in violent spasms. Below, to the west, what was left of that deep sea retreated away from the rising mountains.

There should have been a great deal of green in this image, but there was none. This was a fine range of mountains, but it was a dead landscape that had replaced a dead seafloor. I was in the Late Ordovician time period, and life, especially plants, had not yet managed to colonize the lands. All around me was a bleak, blue-gray landscape. There were not even proper soils, just a litter of gray gravel lying upon bare rocks. Only the dry channels of gullies and ravines broke the monotony of the desolation.

I realized that I had come to the very spot where, 450 million years later, Frederic Church would stand. But I was not seeing what he would see. No, below me and stretching off to the west a large river delta had formed adjacent to the rising Taconic Mountains. A complex of murky streams crossed the dark gray of that delta. Farther away, I could see the retreating waters of the sea. It was bleak and lifeless vista, but there was grandeur in this, Olana's great unplanned view.

Kaatskill Life, Summer 2002

HUDSON RIVER SCHOOL OF ROCKS

SOME YEARS AGO, I attended the national meeting of the Geological Society of America and was surprised to see an agenda with three papers that were devoted to the Hudson River School of Art. Getting papers accepted at the national meeting is a very competitive process so I was surprised that the meeting's organizers would devote so much time to art. What did not surprise me was that it was this particular sort of art. But I bet that this is a bit of a surprise in an artistic community such as Woodstock so let me try to explain.

Thomas Cole, one of the founders of the Hudson River School, got his start here in the Catskills. It was 1825, and he was probably the first painter to get up to the newly opened Catskill Mountain House Hotel. Before him, up there, lay nearly all of the Hudson Valley and behind him were all of the Catskills. It was the Catskill landscape that attracted him the most. This region was still largely wilderness, and the young artist would be the first to explore its scenic opportunities.

Our mountains would bring Cole quick success, but he did have one problem: back then the established traditions of landscape art came from Europe, and it was the custom of European artists to use the ruins of classical cultures as emblems of antiquity. They liked to stick in the remnants of a Roman temple or two in order to communicate that their landscapes were truly old. Obviously Cole could not do this, after all very few Romans ever got to North America during Classical times.

Then again, and this is where my science comes in, Cole was working at a time when geologists were revolutionizing the very concept of time itself. In eighteenth- or early nineteenth-century Europe, a classical ruin was seen as dating back to near the beginning of time, especially if you accepted a biblical estimate of 6,000 years for the age of the Earth. But by the 1820s geologists had come to understand that the Earth was probably many millions of years old and, indeed, very likely much more than that (billions, in fact). A two-thousand-year-old ruin didn't look very old given the new framework of time!

Without ancient monuments, Cole had been struggling to find native emblems of antiquity. He tried the figure of an Indian in his famous painting of Kaaterskill Falls, and that sort of worked. Cole used the tangled chaos of the

American wilderness as another approach. Our wilds had a venerable, tangled and mossy look to them when compared to the tamed, park-like landscapes of Europe. But it wasn't until the 1830s that Cole found another solution: the very rocks themselves.

It's in his *Course of Empire* series that we find Cole using this solution. Course of Empire is his famous set of five landscapes each showing a stage in the history of a mythological Classical empire. The first painting showed that culture's roots in a primitive tribal culture. Later (second painting), it passed into a stone-monolith-building second stage, and from there blossomed into a Roman-like empire (third painting). Sadly, Cole's Empire disintegrated in war (fourth painting) and fell into ruin in the last scene. Throughout the five canvases a great somber mountaintop of rock loomed above the community. And throughout the long history that mountaintop never changed one bit, it was permanent while all below eventually disintegrated. In this way Cole turned the tables on European painters: Classical cultures were recent and ephemeral while the rocks beneath were the true emblems of time.

That was a pretty heady theme in the 1830s and '40s, when Cole was most active. And that same heady theme was central to the geological community of the very same age. We geologists were looking at rocks exactly the same way as Cole and his colleagues; for a moment of time Art and Geology explored the same literal and intellectual landscapes.

Art is ever-changing and, of course, it has moved on. But the notion of great antiquity remains fundamental to geology and geologists integrate it into all of our thinking. Thus, it really is no surprise at all that we geologists still venerate the great Hudson River School of Art. Those paintings speak to us in a very personal way.

Woodstock Times 1999

THE GYPSUM GIANTS

DUST DEVILS are peculiar manifestations of nature's love for the vortex. The dust devil is a sudden, capricious swirling of wind. It needs a hot, sun-broiled ground to generate its intense energy. After forming, it begins to draw in and then capture the dust around it. It spins erratically for a brief time and then dissipates, leaving those dust particles scattered. Human culture has its dust devils. There are events that capture people; they congregate in one location and briefly swirl about each other madly. Curiously, it is often the more strong-willed among us who are most susceptible; they are surprisingly helpless to stay out of the vortex, and they who suffer the most. In the end, more harm than good may come from all this.

One of those cultural dust devils is represented in the Farmer's Museum in Cooperstown. It is one of our most prominent Catskills "citizens." Our dust devil has been in Cooperstown since the 1940s and in that time he has become one of our region's most beloved residents. He is part of our upstate culture: he is the Cardiff Giant.

The Cardiff Giant in repose at Cooperstown. (Titus)

This dust devil swirled during a few weeks of the autumn of 1869; it was the time of the "Gypsum Giants." The Cardiff Giant, itself, was the first of those gypsum personalities, but he is the only one to still be around. He has no proper name, but he is big, ten feet two inches from head to toe. He weighs 2990 pounds. He suffers the humiliation of being naked while on public display. It is only worse that his beard and much the rest of his manhood have been chiseled away.

The Cardiff Giant was the creation of George Hull. He, the second of our gypsum giants, seems to have been a man of many talents and few scruples. He was certainly, for a time, a cigar manufacturer. But there seems to have been little real stability in his life. He is reported to have tried alchemy and to have studied the rudiments of paleontology and archeology. He was a misfit in nineteenth-century culture, being an open atheist in a Christian land. At more than six feet in height and affecting black clothing, he is the embodiment of a real-life "Snidely Whiplash."

His real career and true calling, as a con artist, began by accident. George Hull is reported to have had, one night, a great heated debate with a Reverend Turk. Their conflict was over the many issues of Bible veracity. Evidently the passage "there were giants in the Earth in those days" played a large role in the verbal fisticuffs. That feverish night Hull went to bed pondering that passage and soon, in his imagination, came the genesis of a Genesis hoax. There would be giants, at least one of them, in Hull's times.

Hull traveled to the quarries of Fort Dodge, Iowa, and after "shopping" awhile found just the right block of gypsum. It was twelve feet long, weighed several tons, but most importantly, it had been weathered and dissolved on one side by passing water. In that last point, Hull had used very good judgment. The weathered appearance would make his giant look very old.

Hull transported the gypsum to Chicago and found a stone cutter to carve the giant. Hull, himself, directed every step of the way. His giant would be just anatomically correct enough to pass for a fossil, while, at the same time, it would also look much like a carved statue. People could form their own opinions.

Next, the giant was secretly moved to a farm belonging to his brother-in-law, William "Stub" Newell, in the small town Cardiff, New York, south of Syracuse. It was interred in late November 1868 and left to rest in the ground for a year. The time would allow Nature to provide a look of authenticity to the burial.

In the following November, Stub Newell hired two workman to "dig a well" on his farm. They, of course, hadn't dug too deeply before they "discovered" the gypsum giant. Word spread quickly and people began arriving from all over the surrounding area. The dust devil had begun to spin.

Historians credit George Hull with great insight about the people around him. Cultural dust devils, like the natural ones, require just the right landscape, hot enough to generate the vortex. The Syracuse area was, indeed, just right for Hull's devil. Part of the "burnt over district," the area's evangelical Christians would be very receptive to the "giants-in-the-Earth-in-those-days" hypothesis. Also the area had once been the site of a glacial lake, and ice age bones periodically were discovered here, so much the better for those who would argue for the giant being a fossil. Finally, the area had a rich Indian heritage, perhaps people would suppose that it was they who had carved the giant as a statue. No matter what a person thought of the gypsum giant, the local culture would provide something to back up the view. It was no surprise that a lot of people began visiting the Newell farm.

And, of course, there was money to be made. Stub Newell let people in for free the first day, but soon began charging 50 cents a head to view the giant. He set up a tent so that he could exercise more control over the visitors. The entrepreneurial Newell, with George Hull behind the scenes, was soon awash with cash.

Dust devils don't last long however and George Hull certainly did have good business sense. He had Newell sell a three-quarter interest in the giant for the princely sum of $30,000. The sale was to a Syracuse consortium that would move the giant to a display in that city.

The burning question was simply "what was it?" Only a few people actually thought it was a giant from Biblical times. Instead, there were two prevailing views on what the giant represented. The "petrifactionists" said it was a fossil. If so, it was of enormous scientific importance, a relic from our human past. Most others argued that it was a statue, and if that were so, then it was of very substantial archeological value. Who would decide the issue? The dust devil swirling around the giant would quickly draw more gypsum giants to its center.

On November 5th, a delegation from the New York State Museum in Albany arrived. Chief among them was Professor James Hall, one of America's leading paleontologists and, in fact, one of America's leading scientists. Hall was an eminent man at the peak of his career; he had a powerful personality and was a quintessential "dreadnought" of Victorian culture, a gypsum giant if there ever was one. Hall had been with the New York State Geological Survey since its founding in the 1830s. He had truly distinguished himself with his enormously extensive studies of New York State paleontology. He had nothing to win in Cardiff, but he was a strong man who could not resist the pull of the dust devil.

Hall was warned by Andrew Dickson White, first president of Cornell University, not to stick his neck out on the giant. White understood that there was real danger here; if anybody from the State Museum should make a mistake, it might reflect poorly upon himself and prove an embarrassment to science itself. In short, the stakes were high.

The delegation was treated with great respect, ushered into the tent for a private inspection. Hall was completely drawn into the vortex; he would never get out. Professor Hall, on that day, was too much the scientist. He looked at the details and ignored the obvious. George Hull's choice of stones had been brilliant. The giant had been, in the words of antiquarians, "made to deceive." The solution-pitted underside of the statue fooled James Hall entirely with its beguiling look of antiquity. In the end he pronounced the giant a statue "the most remarkable archaeological discovery ever made in the country . . ."

Hall would not for long be the only respectable paleontologist to visit the statue. Soon, young Othniel Marsh, from Yale University, arrived. Marsh was a man born with a proverbial silver spoon in his mouth. Marsh was the favorite nephew of the great nineteenth-century philanthropist, George Peabody. Uncle Peabody had rescued Marsh from a life on the farm and paid for all of his higher education. After that, Peabody paid for and built the famed Peabody Museum at Yale University. Not surprisingly, young Othniel received a lifetime appointment as professor of paleontology.

In 1869 all this had just recently taken place. Marsh had been given everything except the time to prove himself. But that time had arrived; he was about to prove himself in spades. Marsh had earlier completed his post-graduate education in Europe. There he studied geology and paleontology, but he had the opportunity to learn a good deal about art and availed himself of that. In short, he knew enough to spot a statue; he saw fresh chisel marks. And he was also skeptical enough to know a phony when he saw one. In minutes Marsh was ready to pronounce the Cardiff Giant a "humbug." On November 25th, Marsh published a newspaper letter in which he outlined his conclusions; he had, in very quick time, destroyed the hoax.

Or, I should say, this *should have* destroyed the hoax. Who would want to believe that this was a fake when the other versions were so much more appealing? It is only human nature to go on believing even in the face of certain evidence. Our next gypsum giant would turn that human foible to his advantage. He was the famous, or infamous, Phineus T. Barnum.

Now, the ludicrous graded into the surreal. Barnum did not need to be a scientist to spot a fake a mile away. But he greatly admired the audacity of the whole affair and immediately offered to buy the giant. Refused, the unabashed Barnum simply hired a craftsman to carve a new giant for him. Soon this hoax-of-a-hoax went on display just a few blocks from the "real" giant and, with Barnum's marketing skills, the imitation fake far out-grossed the real fake in terms of gate receipts (did you follow that?).

In the end, the Cardiff Giant was, fundamentally, an iniquitous invention; George Hull meant it to be a fraud from the beginning. So it is curious to find that this dust devil helped more people than it harmed. George Hull made a ton of money as did a number of others, particularly P. T. Barnum.

The biggest winner of all may well have been Othniel Marsh. He had been right about the giant and that presaged a lustrous career for this young paleontologist. Marsh had been born with that silver spoon in his mouth, but it would not keep him from being a very fine scientist. Today, he is best remembered for having discovered the rich dinosaur remains in the Morrison Formation of the American West. This was the original "Jurassic Park," and Marsh made the best of it. He discovered, for science, scores on new species of dinosaurs. He is credited as being a founder of dinosaur science and vertebrate paleontology itself. He had a great and long career in paleontology, and it hadn't hurt him that he had been right about the Cardiff Giant.

Gypsum is a soft mineral, however, and it scratches easily. There was one big loser in the sordid affair, and that was James Hall. He had called the giant a great archeological discovery and, in that, he had blundered badly. No wonder he was looking to change the subject, and, fortunately, he quickly found the chance. As luck would have it, an autumn storm had recently swept through the Catskills and floods in Schoharie Creek had uncovered a number of fossil tree stumps of Devonian age. These were trees of the "Gilboa Forest," a genuinely great paleontological discovery. Hall quickly traveled to Gilboa and recognized the importance of the find. He now had something that he wanted to talk about and he spoke loudly.

But, still, it had been a great embarrassment to the man and a bad misstep in an otherwise distinguished sixty-year career. James Hall would survive and go on to enjoy the last thirty of those years. However, whenever, somebody new came to work for Professor Hall, they were taken aside and very carefully warned to never ever bring up the subject of the Cardiff Giant. There had been, sadly, one gypsum giant too many.

PART TWO

The Catskill Sea

"A HOT TIME IN THE OLD TOWN ... "

LIKE MANY READERS OF *THE INDEPENDENT*, I enjoyed reading excerpts from Margaret Schramm's new history of the city of Hudson. Hudson is an old town with a venerable history and her account covers a lot of that history. I, of course, am a geologist and my idea of history extends a lot farther back into time. I see the city of Hudson as a place which has been here since the formation of the Earth.

It has a geological history and glimpses of that history can sometimes be seen in the rocks. I recently had the experience of seeing such a moment of time when I traveled one mile south on County Route 29, from its intersection with Route 23B. At that location, the road is funneled through a narrow passage. Claverack Creek closes in from the east and a large cliff rises to the west.

My attention was on the rocks. I pulled over and began to look them over. The unit was familiar to me; it is the Manlius Limestone, something that I see all across New York State. It's thinly-bedded, fine-grained strata took me back about 400 million years to a time when most of New York State was submerged by the shallow waters of the Helderberg Sea.

This was a very warm sea; North America lay just a little south of the equator. The "city of Hudson" was enjoying a very tropical climate at that time.

The thin laminations of the Manlius tell us a lot about what the city of Hudson was like back in the early Devonian. They are the product of what are called algal mats. Once this was a mud flat and sheets of primitive algae grew on its surface. You might have to travel as far as the Persian Gulf so see something like this today. But there is much more to see here.

There was a fine overhang in the cliff right where I parked. When I looked up at the stratum exposed beneath it, I was surprised to see one of those little wonders of geology; that surface was covered with mud cracks.

Mud cracks (Titus)

Mud cracks are imprints that formed at approximately the time of deposition. They speak to us of a moment in time 400 million years ago. Mud cracks are also called desiccation cracks, which is to say that they formed at a time when the sediment was baking in the sun.

I reached up and touched the surface. To touch such a rock is to literally be in contact with the past. Now I became a time traveler, and in my mind's eye, I was back in the early Devonian and on that mud flat. I had arrived at noon on a clear day in August. The sun's heat seemed to pound down on the surface. There was not even the slightest of breezes, and the hot air pooled on the ground. In the distance, I could see rising currents of air distorted by the heat. This is the stuff of mirages and near the horizon there was the appearance of an expanse of water.

But there was no water. In fact, recent months had witnessed a terrible drought. The ground was bare marine sediment, and it positively blistered in the sun. Over time, all moisture had been baked out of it. The sediment then slowly shrank and, as it did so, it began to pull into polygonal masses bordered by polygonal cracks.

If you ever get a chance to see a pond, which has dried up in some summer drought, you will see the same thing today. But I was in the Devonian, and parched mud cracks stretched out in all directions. It was surreal, something Salvador Dali might well have enjoyed painting.

And it was a dead landscape. I felt very small and alone in this inhospitable Devonian land. Then I pulled my hand away from the rock and all around me was the cool greenery of a late spring. This is Hudson as it is today, but not as it has always been.

The Independent, July 2004

THE FINEST CATSKILL MARBLE

OUR CATSKILLS are renowned for their bluestone. It makes wonderful side-walks and curbs, patios, and even building stone. But how many people think of the Catskills as a source for fine quality marble? Not many, I would imagine. Marble conjures up images of distant quarries in far away countries. Italy is the source of some of the best marbles, and there such Renaissance finery somehow seems right. But the Catskills? Ours is a rustic land in which bluestone is the perfect rustic stone; marble just doesn't seem right. Well, maybe not.

I have to be careful here to define what I mean. The word *marble* has several definitions. To a geologist, such as myself, who wants to be precise in his use of geological terms, the word has a very specific meaning. Marble is formed when limestone is subjected to intense heat and pressure, usually deep within the Earth's crust. We say that the heat and pressure metamorphose the limestone and destroy its original structure. Limestone is a sedimentary rock that forms on the bottom of a shallow tropical sea. It is usually richly fossiliferous and makes a fine historical record of its time. With marble the fossils have been cooked out of existence and the original stratification is obliterated. The rock is robbed of most of its original "personality" and we lose its history. But the process does create an attractive stone that can be cut and polished and used for a variety of purposes. Many a tabletop is made of marble. Sometimes, too, it can be carved into statuary or even cathedrals.

But there is a broader meaning of the word *marble*. Few people care about the ancient limestone seas. What they are interested in is attractive stone, especially when it can be fashioned into elegant furniture. Many types of stone are referred to as marble, all that really counts is that the stuff looks good. Strangely, limestone itself can sometimes be called marble, and that gets us to the Catskill variety. My story today is about a rock unit that is called the Becraft Limestone. It is a commonly exposed unit of rock in the Hudson Valley, just below the Catskill Front. It takes us back about 400 million years to the early Devonian time period.

Most limestone is pretty dull stuff; it is usually a very drab gray color, and it attracts the eyes of only a few. That's ironic because the seafloors on which limestone sediments accumulate are colorful and rich with fascinating living creatures. If you have ever gone snorkeling in Florida or in the Bahamas, then you know of what I speak. Jacques Cousteau built a career on such seafloors.

But, as I said, limestone is pretty dull stuff. It's easily cut and polished, and it does look better in that state, but usually it is so brittle that it breaks up before it can be made into anything useful. And even when polished, it's still usually a boring looking material. There are exceptions, and the Becraft Limestone is a very good one. You see the Becraft sediments accumulated on a shallow tropical seafloor in which something unusual happened. Limestone is composed of calcium carbonate ($CaCO_3$) and generally little else, but in much of the Becraft there is also some iron oxide (hematite which is Fe_2O_3). There is just a little hematite, but it has a blood-red color and it is a very good pigment. That gives what would have been a dull gray limestone a very handsome color and texture.

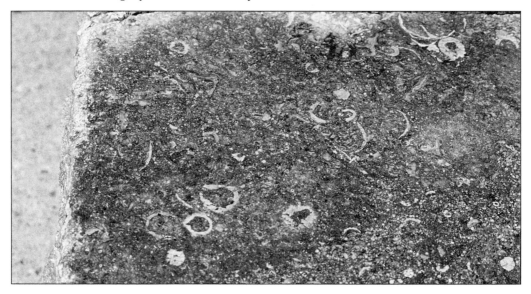

Close-up of the Becraft Limestone. (Titus)

There is more. The Becraft seafloor was very rich in marine shellfish. These were studied during the 1930s by New York State Paleontologist Winifred Goldring, who was also a talented artist. One of her illustrations was devoted to the Becraft. Most of the fossils are from a shellfish group called the brachiopods. These invertebrates have two shells, just as the clams do, but they are not clams; they have a very different anatomy. Brachiopod shells are very common in the Becraft, and when the rock is cut and polished, they add a great deal to the attractiveness of the rock. But there is one more very peculiar fossil type found in the Becraft. That is a strange creature called a crinoid by paleontologists and a sea lily by everyone else. Sea lilies are animals, but they resemble plants; they have long "stems" and attach themselves to the seafloor with root-like structures called holdfasts or scutellas. In life they come in many bright colors, and this flowery appearance heightens the plant resemblance. Sea lilies were often so densely pop-

**Fossils of the Becraft Limestone, mostly brachiopods,
illustration by Winifred Goldring. (Courtesy, New York State Museum)**

ulated on the old Devonian-age seafloor that they can be said to have formed
oceanic "meadows." This was certainly the case with the Becraft seafloor. The
holdfast structures are very large and enormously abundant. They make up a
large percentage of the limestone.

All in all, the rich red color and the abundant fossils make the Becraft

Limestone a very attractive stone. It came to be called marble, using the loosest definition of the word, and, back in the nineteenth century, people opened up quarries where they found deposits that could be cut into large slabs. I am not sure exactly where those quarries were but many of them were likely to have been in or around the region of the village of Catskill. There must have been a thriving trade in this "marble" because there is a lot of this stone. Marble must have contributed to the local economy, and that is one of the reasons that Catskill was once a very affluent community.

You can go and see some of the signs of that affluence yourself. Travel into Catskill and find the Greene County Courthouse. The building itself, including its fine columns is built of Indiana limestone, which is pretty good stone. A very large amount of the Becraft marble also went into the construction of the facility. There is an especially nice wall all along the front of the building. When I visited it, I brought along a squeeze bottle of water and hosed down the stone. That brought out the color and highlighted the fossils of the Becraft. I could clearly see the many crinoid holdfasts and brachiopod shells in the stone.

Just around the corner is the famous old Presbyterian Church with its six beautiful Corinthian columns. Many of the nineteenth-century worshipers here must have been very wealthy and, as they built the church, they used the finest materials. This, of course, included a great deal of Becraft marble all along the front of the building. I found the stone here had become a bit weathered over time, but it must have been a handsome stuff when first cut.

The very best Becraft marble that I have found is in the village of Leeds. The famous Leeds Bridge dates back to the 1790s and it was rebuilt and modernized in the 1930s. The bridge is entirely composed of Becraft Limestone, and the artisans that fabricated it had the good judgement to use the best slabs as capstone along to two sides of the bridge. If you can go there, please park and walk slowly across on the bridge sidewalks. You will see some very fine stone here. The slabs were selected for their rich assemblages of well-preserved fossils. I found lots of brachiopods and crinoids, but I also found a wealth of other types of creatures. There are corals and snails and trilobites to be seen here. It really is something of an outdoor museum of the Devonian seafloor and it deserves to be appreciated.

Unfortunately, the Becraft does not hold its polish well in the outdoors. It is easily dissolved by rainwater, especially when there is acid rain. The nice shine disappears, and the details of the fossils become invisible. None of this is a problem indoors however, and much of the finest of Becraft stone was cut into nineteenth-century tabletops. The stone takes a very nice polish, and with its red color and many fossil fragments, it is a very attractive material. I have seen examples in a number of antique shops so it must have once been a popular choice for furniture tops.

The Greene County courthouse in Catskill. *Below:* The Leeds Bridge. (Titus)

Nineteenth-century Becraft Limestone table. (Titus)

Sadly, it appears that the old quarries are now depleted. It would seem that this most elegant of Catskill products is off the market. I could not find anyone in the stone trade who could even identify the Becraft. Still, you never know where you will see such things . . .

* * *

My wife and I entered the Graystone Inn in West Martinsburg, way up in the Black River Valley. There, in the old 1805 entrance hall was an antique table with a wonderful Becraft marble top. It is always a pleasure for me to find such a good example. I instinctively reached out and ran my fingers across its cool, smooth surface, and I gazed into the stone looking to identify the fossils and other grains within it. To touch a sedimentary rock like this is to literally be in contact with the distant past. My hand touches a special past and I am transported:

April 3rd, 402,681,345 years BC, early morning: It has been a beautiful morning over the Catskill Sea. The sky has been partly cloudy and the winds have blown gently across the clear waters. They have produced a continuous set of waves from due west. The seas are very shallow and the seafloor is well illuminated by the tropical sun. This sea bottom is densely populated by sea lilies. They come in a spectrum of colors, but yellow, red, and green forms predominate. They rock back and forth in the wave-generated currents. Their arms reach into the waters and collect microscopic bits of food. These sea lilies make up the "flowers" of a

Opposite: **The Presbyterian Church in the village of Catskill. (Titus)**

Devonian age marine meadow. All around them are the seaweeds that make up the "grass" of the same meadow. It is a beautiful sea bottom. Here and there are brightly colored shellfish, bivalved brachiopods. There is an occasional clam as well. Crawling slowly near the bottom is a small cluster of snails.

By late morning, it is warming up quickly, with temperatures climbing into the middle 80s. In mid-afternoon the sky quickly clouds up and darkens. Now there are strong winds and approaching flashes of lightning. The waves are tall, and they approach faster now. Quickly, an intense storm strikes. It is only the first of several lines of squalls that are bearing down on what will someday be the Catskills.

Soon the waves intensify and a steady current begins to rake the sea bottom. The sea lilies and seaweeds are waving back and forth quickly, and soon this graduates to a thrashing motion. Great masses of silt and clay are lofted up from the seafloor and the waters become cloudy and gray. It is hard for the snails, and they are vainly seeking shelter.

Now the currents are actively dragging the sea bottom. The sea lily stems are breaking up and the dying animals are being swept away. The pink sediments are turning into a swirling, churning fluid, moving like a current across the turbulent seafloor. The brachiopods have little hope; they are being buried and will be unable to dig themselves out after the storm passes. This will be a deadly day.

Above, the sea is a dark gray, foaming mass. The winds are howling across it and driving storm rollers that are cresting and moving rapidly toward the east. The waters are dirty and turbulent with their heavy load of silt and clay. It is a submarine version of the1930's dust bowl. Below, now there is a six-inch thick layer of actively moving sediment. It seems alive as it moves as a sheet across the sea bottom. The lowest inch or so is heavy stuff, buried shellfish, while the rest is largely composed of lighter sea lily fragments. All the clay, silt and fine-grained sand is being swept far away.

By the end of this awful day the storms have passed and things have settled down. Where there had been colorful marine meadows now there is the barren desolation of a fresh half-foot thick deposit of coarse sediment. Few creatures are still alive; many have been broken up into a shell hash. As the sun sets and the seafloor darkens, the last of the finer, lighter sediments is settling out of suspension like a dust. The new deposit is settling itself and compacting under its own weight. It is beginning a long process that will very slowly turn it into a fine stone, something that people will call marble . . . .

* * *

I took my hand off the table and we went to the dining room for a very nice meal.

Kaatskill Life, Winter 2003

JOURNEY TO THE BOTTOM OF THE SEA

WE GEOLOGISTS, over and over, are used to seeing vivid moments from the past recorded in the rocks. We never become blasé about this, and we shouldn't; we are privileged to have these visions. I was reminded of this recently when I encountered an especially fine outcrop along Route 9W at Glenerie, about a mile and a half south from its intersection with the Glasco Turnpike. It's the Helderberg Limestone, which is commonly seen along the highway hereabouts. There was one very broad surface which caught my attention. It's a bed of rock so steep that I found it difficult to climb, but that mattered little as the bed slanted down to the level of the road. The strata, dipping to the west, are typical of this vicinity. These rocks got caught up and tilted in the deformation associated with ancient mountain building in New England.

What makes this such a fine exposure is that there is one particular stratum which is expansively exposed. That's unusual. We geologists spend a lot of time looking at strata in cross section, but we rarely get to see a broad surface like this. Once again, I had become a time-traveler; this bit of geology had taken me back in time to the early Devonian time period. I don't mean that figuratively, but quite literally; this stratum of sedimentary rock was deposited on the floor of a sunlit shallow sea nearly 400 million years ago. For a time, it actually was the seafloor and upon it grew the seaweeds and crawled the shellfish of the old Devonian age sea.

But time is fleeting, even geological time. Sooner or later (and in geology it really can be later) a seafloor is condemned to be buried. Storms blow up and the winds generate currents which bring new masses of sediment to be spread about. Many of the plants and animals that populated the old seafloor remain, but only as fossils. Layer after layer of sediment piles up and the seafloors of old harden into strata of rock lost in time. That's what geologists see in cross section when they study layered road outcrops such as most of those on Route 9W.

But not all of the strata here have shared that inglorious fate. There is, for example, this one fine stratum. It's an example of something unusual, an exhumed seafloor. Nature (helped a lot by the highway department) has stripped the overburden off of this old seafloor and exposed it for us to see.

You have, quite likely, been on a boat that cruised above the floor of a shallow sea. It's a lot of fun; you can look down and observe the marine life going by below. Glass-bottom boats are specifically designed for this. In Florida or the Bahamas you can't beat them for a fascinating afternoon. It's nice that we can do the same thing right here in Ulster County.

Our stratum, along Route 9W, can't quite compete with a glass-bottom boat in the Bahamas. All of the old seaweeds are gone, so too are most of the animals. All those creatures without skeletons or with only delicate skeletons are lost to time. Only those shellfish that had sturdy shells remain, but there are plenty of them. I found quite a few brachiopods, those bivalved shellfish that remind us of clams. They occurred in clusters of specimens, all about the same size. I think that these are what biologists call "spat falls," clusters of larval brachiopods that settled here and grew up together. These are "families" of shellfish, if you can imagine such a thing. I found a few clams here as well, but they weren't common. Finally, I found the weathered and forlorn tail of a trilobite, all which remained of a once fine-looking creature. All in all, what I was looking at was a snapshot of the old Devonian seafloor, just a moment in time, nothing special, and maybe that's why it is special.

The Route 9W outcrop at Glenerie. (Titus)

Because of its steepness, this old seafloor is difficult to climb around on. If you visit the site, be very careful. One slip and down you go. The fact is, however, that there is no real need to climb up the exposure at all, most all the good things you can see are found at the base of the outcrop. There's no real need to climb any higher. So do go and see this little natural wonder. You don't get many opportunities to explore a seafloor, especially one that existed 400 million years ago.

Woodstock Times, Apr. 1998

THE WORM TURNS

ALONG ROUTE 9W at Glenerie, the Esopus Creek descends two ledges of rock known as the Glenerie Limestone. These ledges make up what are either high rapids or low waterfalls, depending on your point of view. In any case, they also make a very nice setting, and the shores of the Esopus there attract a lot of people. I sat on the banks for a while and watched people go by. There were two fishermen, who had no luck. A couple walked by with their dogs. Several young boys came by on their bicycles. One elderly man wandered along the shore, I think just for the pleasure of it.

Such is life for human beings who are not at work, but just intent upon enjoying a little leisure. The Glenerie Falls provides a setting to idle away a few minutes or a few hours. As I sat along the Esopus, I was watching just a few random moments in the history of life. Nothing special occurred, nothing historic or even meriting the slightest of note. Most of what goes on in this world is like that. Little that happens is really of very much significance. Such is life.

It's easy to forget that this spot has always been here. The world is four-and-one-half billion years old and this precise longitude and latitude has been here all of that time. What was it like here a century ago? I don't know, but with the help of a historian I could easily guess. How about 500 years ago? A little harder, but good guesses might come from an archeologist. How about a million? or a hundred million? or a billion years ago? Even a geologist has a hard time answering those questions.

So much of earth history slips off into the past without leaving any monument or even a clue as to what had transpired. But none of these moments is likely to have amounted to much, just simple events during average times. Countless living creatures have passed by the Glenerie Falls site and almost all are gone and have been entirely forgotten by history. Disappearing into the oblivion of the past is a sad fate that we all share eventually . . . almost all.

But sometimes, hundreds of millions of years after their deaths, signs of the lives of ancient creatures return to light. And I mean that very literally. Memories of ancient organisms are often revived when weathering and erosion of bedrock brings to surface the evidence of lives long lost. We geologists call these "trace fossils." They are not the bones or shells of ancient organisms, but the evidences of ancient activity, the very behaviors of the past. The best known trace fossils are dinosaur footprints. People have marveled at them for more than a century. They forget that these "marvels" are only evidence of the most everyday and literally pedestrian moments in the lives of dinosaurs. Unfortunately we don't have dinosaurs or their footprints anywhere near Woodstock. But we do have other trace fossils.

A lower ledge of the Glenerie Limestone forms the lower cataract of the falls. The rock is tough and brittle stuff and it has held up well against the elements. On the bank, just below Route 9W, this ledge has been brought to the surface by folding of the bedrock. The upper surface of the inclined stratum is a fossil wonder. It's densely littered with the trace fossils of worms that lived here about a little less than 400 million years ago.

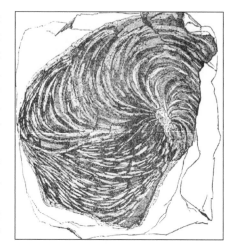

The worm burrow Zoophycos. (Courtesy, New York State Museum)

The animal has a name—it's *Zoophycos*. It was a common marine worm, much like many that live today. You probably know that earthworms make their living by burrowing through soil, consuming and digesting it as they slowly move forward. Similarly *Zoophycos* burrowed and ate its way through the marine sediments, including the limestone sediments of the Glenerie. *Zoophycos* was extremely meticulous in the way it dined on sediment. It burrowed forward for a while, its path taking it in a broad, round loop. The worm then turned abruptly and returned, closely paralleling its first path. Then, once again, it turned on a dime and paralleled its second path. Back and forth it continued, carefully consuming all of the sediment. Eventually the back and forth path took on the form of a rooster tail, and that is the common name it goes by. Rooster tails are abundant throughout the marine sandstones and shales of the Catskills, but this is the first time I have seen them in a limestone. They are fascinating and marvelous fossils, offering detailed insights into the details of ancient life, but they record such mundane moments: worms eating mud!

If you carefully examine this ledge of rock, you will be surprised at how densely burrowed it is. A large population of these worms must have lived here. To survive on a limited food resource, they had to evolve the careful feeding patterns that we see. I doubt they missed anything. There is, I suspect, a message here.

Woodstock Times, June 1997

END OF AN ERA:
THE DEVONIAN OF GREENE COUNTY, PART SIX

NEW BALTIMORE'S LIMEKILN ROAD runs south-to-north in the very pretty northeast corner of Greene County. It's steeped in history, and as I am sure you can guess, much of that history is centered on a lime kiln. To drive there, first head east from Greenville on Route 26, go 9.7 miles east from Stewart's Shop, turn left onto Limekiln Road and continue north. You will go exactly one and three quarters miles north to get to your destination, but don't be in a hurry. A little more than a mile along the way you will see the lime kiln itself on the left side of the road. A historic marker states that the kiln goes back to the 1850s, but it's still in a very good state of repair. It must have been quite the operation back then because there has been a lot of quarrying along the road. Watch carefully and you will see remains of the excavations that once fed limestone into the kiln. The rock ended up as lime and fertilizer.

As I said, there is a lot of history here. But we will find that this nineteenth-century history has allowed us to see into a much deeper period of the past. Continue north another half mile along the road and you will soon see pools of water just to the right (east) side of the road. Here more of the old quarrying carved out a rough basin. Quarries always provide geologists with keyholes into the distant past; this is a very good keyhole.

The quarry speaks to us of an important episode of our area's history, when there was the return of another shallow tropical sea, once again something very much like the Bahamas of today. Go here and you will visit some very nice limestones. These are called the Onondaga Limestone, and they have quite a story to tell.

Limestone is the sort of rock that originates in shallow tropical seas. Visit the western coast of Florida, famed for its shell collecting, and you will see just exactly this sort of habitat. Fossil rich limestones are forming there today. Travel to the southern tip of Florida and go snorkeling, and you just might be fortunate enough to be able to explore a coral reef. Someday, some of these reefs will harden into limestone and become fossil coral reefs.

As you will probably guess, we don't have to go to Florida, or the Bahamas, to see such wonders; our trip to Limekiln Road has brought us to a very good one.

Above us is an inconspicuous hill named Roberts Hill. It's a pretty little place but not the sort of landscape that would attract much notice. But look above you and through the woods; you will see a number of outcroppings of limestone. A closer look will tell you something most remarkable: this hill, all of it, is a fossil coral reef. See for yourself. At first you only halfway notice inconspicuous gray outcrops, but close up it is all very different. The rock is "alive" with corals. You have to see this to believe it, but it is there. The reef even has a name; it's called the Robert's Hill Reef.

Stand along the side of the road and gaze up at Roberts Hill. Now your mind's eye must travel back in time. It is the Devonian, and all around you are the agitated waters of the tropical Onondaga Sea. Rising in front of us is the murky image of a great coral reef. Immediately in front of us are a number of coral mounds. Rising above these are the skinny arms of branched corals; these colorful arms seem to reach out towards the water's surface. Farther up, near the top of the reef, we see a large cluster of smaller and shorter corals. Each of these has the shape of a cow's horn.

Look straight up and you will see the undersides of passing waves. They sparkle in the sun as the swells and troughs pass overhead. The waves are approaching the reef from behind us (the southwest). Our eyes can follow any of these waves and watch as it closes in on, and then smashes into, the reef in front of us. The collision stirs up a chaos of bubbles and silt. Together, these materials make our view of the reef an indistinct and cloudy one. Below and behind us is the rubble of broken dead corals. This litter records damaging episodes of intense wave activity. Roberts Reef can be a very rough place to live.

On the day of our mind's eye visit, the waves are quite strong and few animals are venturing out. The corals are well adapted to the stress but all the fish have hunkered down. They are hiding in the reef's many nooks and crannies, and they are out of sight. It's too bad about that. Suddenly, an especially great wave crashes into the reef and our image of it is completely obscured. In a flash we are back in the present and the summer greenery replaces our view of the reef. It's nice to look at but just not the same.

Our trip into the past was too brief, but let's use what we learned to make the best of it. This outcrop is a hash of whole and broken corals, probably preserving most of the original reef. Take a look and see for yourself. I found the best fossil hunting in the roadside knob just south of that small pool of water. You won't have to climb around very much; the nearby exposed rocks there show most of what you need to see. The land is posted so we should stick close to the road.

There are three broad categories of corals to look for. The biggest are not the most common and not the easiest to find, but they are worth the effort. They are the old coral heads that grew into mound-like forms. Look for large dark corals, up to two or three feet across and focus on the detail. You can identify these from

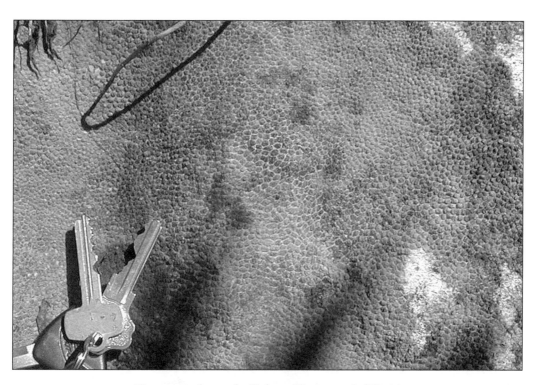

Honeycomb coral. *Below:* **Horn coral. (Titus)**

Digitate coral. (Titus)

the honeycomb patterns within them. Each honeycomb chamber was once inhabited by a single coral animal so the coral head makes up a colonial structure, coral apartment houses. The second type of coral can be recognized by its circular shape. Watch for something that sort of looks like the cross section of a gray orange. The appearance is misleading as the whole specimen actually has a horn shape. It's only the cross sectional view that looks circular. These, logically enough, are called "horn corals." They lived in clusters on the reef. The third type is a digitate coral. In this case, a number of corals grew together in branches (digits) that reached up toward the currents. You will mostly find cylindrical fragments of their branches, often with many of them lying parallel to each other.

If you have never seen anything like this before, I think you will find it to be most remarkable. Look all around you; today it is Greene County in high summer and all around the greenery is beautiful to see, the air fresh to breath. But we have already looked at all this with the eyes of geologists; all around us we have seen the relentless wave pounding of a sparkling shallow tropical sea. We have seen reef corals reaching out to these waves. We have found that this space, back in the Devonian, was a very, very different place indeed.

If you make your return trip down Limekiln Road, watch for two more exposures of the Onondaga Limestone along the way; they are fine cliffs on the right (west) side of the road. Notice that with these outcrops there are no fossil corals. These strata expose a different environment of the Onondaga. These well-stratified limestones formed in the open ocean; a habitat without any reefs. It seems that the Onondaga Sea was too deep here to allow coral reefs to get established. The reefs are all found to the north; in the south the ocean was different open-ocean ecology.

All this represents an end of an era. After the Onondaga there would never again be a time of such shallow tropical seas in Greene County. Our county would never again resemble the Bahamas; a major period in its history was over.

Greenville Press, July 21, 2005

DEPTHS OF DEPRESSION

THE SINKING OF THE *TITANIC* is one of the great stories of history. It's complete with drama, heroism, and even, despite the inevitable ending, suspense. Throw in a little romance and no wonder that the movie was such a hit. Part of the movie's success was the allure of the deep. The ocean's great mysterious abyssal plain retains, even today, a compelling fascination. To scientists, however, equally gripping was the story of the discovery of the sunken liner. You may remember it. Intrepid oceanographers from Woods Hole, Massachusetts, descended to the depths of the ocean's great abyss in tiny submarines. Powerful headlights shined upon the long unseen seafloor and then upon the wreckage itself. What an incredible moment! The substance of fiction became history.

The depths of the seas had long been shrouded in mystery, and to see actual film from the deep is one of the great achievements of the twentieth century, certainly ranking with anything that our space programs have achieved. Much of the abyss is monotonous mud, but there are those many shipwrecks, and a whole exotic ecology of truly wondrous and intriguing animals.

All of this imagery is made even more appealing by the seeming impossibility of traveling to the bottom of the deep sea. Few of us, after all, get invitations from Woods Hole. If you could visit the great abyss, would you leap at the chance, or would you shrink from the real danger of the journey? Would a good movie be

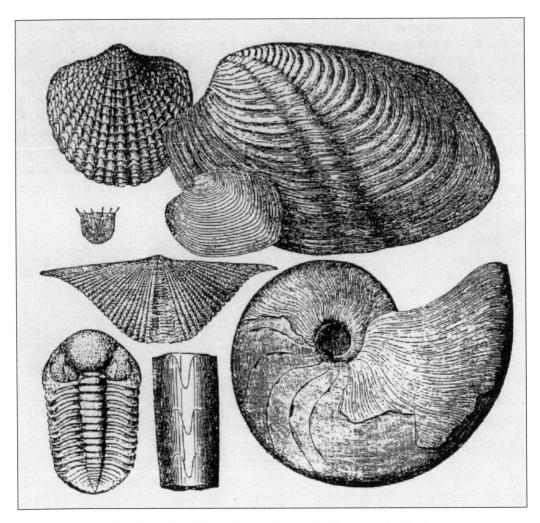

Fossils of the Devonian seafloor. (Author's collection)

enough or would you have the adventurous streak needed for that perilous trek to the very bottom of the deep? It is dangerous; people have died down there.

Let's make it easy. I can have you onto the abyss in about half an hour, and it will be no more dangerous than a short car ride from Woodstock. Take the Glasco Turnpike east from Woodstock until you approach Mount Marion. Look for John Carle Road and turn right and head south along it. The path of the road is like that of a sinking ocean liner. First it strays only just a little from its straight path. Then, as if filling up with water, it veers sharply to the left and rapidly descends a steep slope. Near the bottom, it lurches sharply to the right and settles, once more, onto a flat floor. And indeed, like a sinking ship, the road has arrived at the bottom of a sea.

There is nothing figurative in my remarkable claim; this is really the bottom of a sea. Or it was a long time ago. Rising to the right of the road is a cliff of dark black sandstone and shale. These accumulated at the bottom of a deep sea, one that was here nearly 400 million years ago. It can be called the Catskill Sea, and the layers of rock you see here were once the mud that made up its bottom.

It's a curious thing, but way back then, the Devonian time period, most of New England was rising into a substantial mountain range. These, the Acadian Mountains, would reach heights of maybe 30,000 feet. As they were rising, however, the crust of the adjacent vicinities, including today's Hudson Valley, became depressed. Given time, a fairly substantial deep sea was produced. How deep? I don't know. It would not have rivaled the depths of the North Atlantic, but it was a still, mud-bottomed, dark and very silent seafloor.

Much of the roadside exposure is thinly bedded black shale. That was the mud. Those layers piled up slowly over uncounted centuries. Each thin horizon was once the seafloor. With time, another and then another seam of mud would accumulate. As the weight piled up, the mud was squeezed and hardened into shale.

The dark sandstones are somewhat different. These were more active influxes of sediment, moments when masses of sand tumbled into the depths.

There were living creatures at the bottom of this sea. It only took me a short time to find fossil shellfish here, small animals that spent their whole lives on this quiet sea bottom. No crashing ocean liners interrupted their lives. Scientists did come and visit them, but not until nearly 400 million years after their deaths.

Woodstock Times, March 1998

THE POISON SEA

THE CATSKILLS rarely have a season of "dog days," the time of hot, humid, heavy, stagnant air. That weather is the lot of more southerly climes. Up here, more often than not, our summers are nearly ideal: warm, dry and pleasant. However, that was not always the case. The rocks contain the record of a very different time in the history of our region, a very long time of perpetually unpleasant summer.

Drive along U.S. Route 20 in the vicinity north of Cherry Valley, and you will see some remarkable rocks, the jet-black strata of a unit of rock called the

Chittenango Shale. All sedimentary rocks represent ancient environments, but it usually takes a while to decipher their histories. The Chittenango communicates its story as soon as it is seen. Its strata are thinly bedded sedimentary rocks, which were once the mud of an ancient ocean's seafloor.

I last visited these rocks late in March with my stratigraphy class. At the time, a late winter snow flurry was approaching. In the cold, cloudy sky, the Chittenango is an almost sinister looking sequence of rock: dark, forbidding, and mysterious. And that's exactly what it once was because the Chittenango records the history of the "poison sea" which once covered the western Catskill region.

Go back about 380 million years. At that time, a great mountain-building event was going on throughout western New England. The Acadian Mountains

**The Chittenango Shale makes up the upper reaches of this outcrop on Route 20.
(Titus)**

were rising to elevations of perhaps 30,000 feet. (They've nearly eroded away now; only the Berkshires remain as remnants). To their west was the Catskill Sea, which covered much of North America. Throughout most of its great expanse this ocean was quite shallow, maybe only a few hundred feet, maybe less. However, the nearshore waters, immediately west of the rising Acadian Mountains, were quite deep. It's a curious phenomenon, but, as a mountain range rises, the adjacent crust often subsides. The resulting north-south lying basin of water can be called the "poison sea."

It was the geography of the time that made the poison sea. The Catskill vicinity then lay in tropical latitudes so that the climate was quite warm, and so was

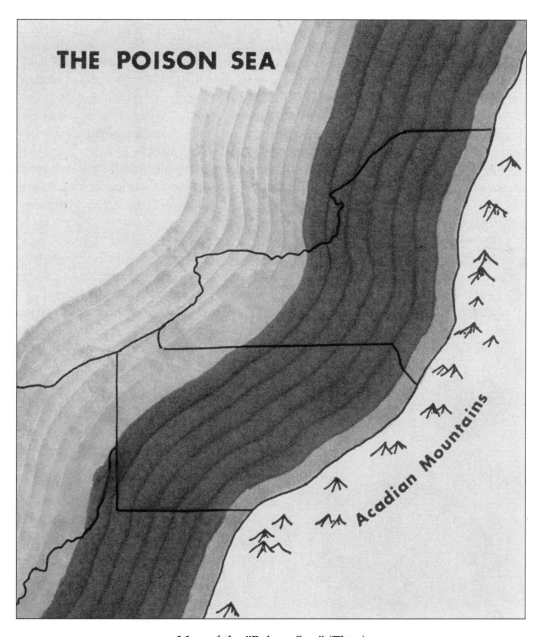

Map of the "Poison Sea." (Titus)

the ocean. The ancient Acadian Mountains blocked the weather patterns which otherwise would have approached, riding along on the easterly trade winds. That's the important part. You see, with the weather patterns blocked, there was relatively little wind blowing across the Catskill Sea and thus few currents to churn up that ocean. West of the Acadian Mountains, the sheltered sea became a hot, stagnant "soup."

We can visit similar seas today. The Black Sea, though not on the equator, is a good example. Being land-locked, weather patterns do not much affect the Black Sea. The waters of such seas are usually stratified. Although the surface waters are very warm, they do contain a lot of oxygen and sea creatures can and do flourish in these shallow waters. It is different below; there bacteria consume all of the oxygen and the sea water becomes anoxic, making it "poisonous" for any creatures who may wander in. They don't; these waters are lifeless.

Such conditions persist right down to the bottom. As is normally the case with oceans, mud accumulates on the seafloor. The mud of oxygen-poor seas is always jet black in color, and when it is compressed and hardened into rock, it becomes black shale. That's how the Chittenango Shale formed.

Meanwhile, at the surface of the Catskill Sea, conditions were different. There was plenty of oxygen and a flourishing community of marine life. Green masses of floating algae, with many small animals, thrived as a rich planktonic ecology, an oceanic jungle. Today we often call such a marine community a sargassum.

Floating creatures seldom have skeletons and so they are rarely preserved as fossils. Consequently the Chittenango Shale displays only a few fossils for the

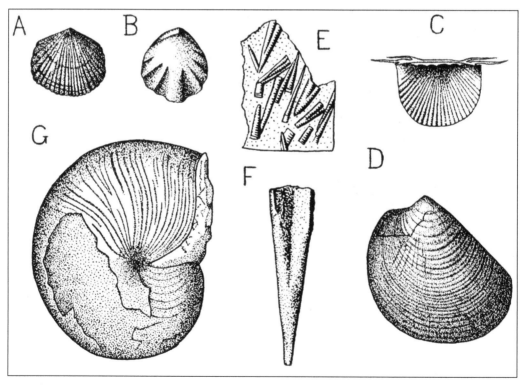

**Fossils of the Poison Sea: A, B, C – brachiopods; D – clam;
E, F -styliolinids; G – nautiloid. (Courtesy, New York State Museum)**

careful hunter to find. Back in the 30's Winifred Goldring, a paleontologist with the New York State Museum, studied the Chittenango and published some fine illustrations. Among her specimens, three (A, B, and C) are tiny shellfish called brachiopods. These will remind you of clams but they aren't; they are an entirely separate group of shellfish. One specimen (D) is a clam. Notice that brachiopod shells have symmetry and the clam's shell doesn't. Pictures E and F are a puzzle. These creatures, called styliolinids, are extinct, and we don't know what they were. That's a common problem with rocks this old.

All of these invertebrates were small and lightweight. They could float in the surface waters of the poison sea, drifting as plankton or attached to floating wood or seaweed. Specimen G is different; it was an active swimmer. We call it a nautiloid, and its descendants are still alive. The chambered nautilus of the south Pacific is today's living nautiloid. Closely related to squids and octopods, the nautiloids had tentacles and well-developed eyes. They were active predators, swimming in the surface waters of the poison seas.

You can visit the poison sea yourself. From Cherry Valley, take County Route 166 northeast to Route 20. Head east on Route 20 and travel 2.6 miles, where you will reach Chestnut Street. There you will find an outcrop with two units of shale separated by about five feet of gray limestone.

If you patiently pick through the shale beds, you will certainly find many styliolinids. You have to search carefully as they are very small. With luck you may find some of the other fossils as well. I have seen some very fine fossil snails below the limestone at the eastern end of the outcrop. That limestone can also be a lot of fun too. This unit represented a temporary break from the poison sea conditions. For a period of time a shallow, oxygenated, tropical sea prevailed here. The limestone has a number of fossils in it, typical of such seas.

The poison seas are misnamed; there were never any active toxins in them, just an absence of oxygen. Nature does that from time to time. The lesson we learn from the poison seas is not that Nature creates inhospitable environments, but that she allows life enough time to adapt to her conditions. The planktonic creatures of the Chittenango Shale thrived just a few feet above one of Nature's most inhospitable environments.

* * *

Visiting the Chittenango is not the same as seeing the poison sea itself. To do that, pick one of those hot, humid, but clear summer days and, in the stillness of the early evening, find a vantage point looking down upon the valley of the Mohawk. The Chestnut Street site will do just fine. From here you can still see the entire expanse of the old poison sea, stretching from the eastern to the western horizons. You are a little above the old sea level, and the atmosphere is just as it was back then. The summer sun is setting in the northwest and, as it approaches the horizon, the valley of the Mohawk darkens and flattens into a land of somber colors.

The fields become a brownish, algae green; the forests turn jet black; to the northwest, the horizon becomes the image of a very still sea. Back to the east there is a distant bank of clouds. As this eastern horizon darkens, those clouds sharpen into the clear vision of the peaks of the ancient Acadian Mountains. Distant mountain ranges often masquerade as clouds, and there is always a shock of surprise when one recognizes the illusion. The lower Acadian slopes are dark blue and brown; they are already in the shade. The jagged pinnacles are small brilliant pyramids; they still reflect the sun.

The air is absolutely still and the surface of the poison sea is as flat as water can be. Gauzy green clouds of algae alternate with bottomless pools of black waters. Occasionally, bubbles of fetid gas rise to the surface of the sea, and oily dots mar the blackness. Only these betray the suffocating gloom in the depths below. Small, delicate wakes mar the perfect flatness; unseen predators are hunting unseen prey. Now a few swells pass heading westward, waves reflected off the distant coast. The green algae patches lazily drift back and forth in these oceanic breezes. Abruptly there is a disturbance, a quick splash and, for a split second, a mass of tentacles, a single eye and then a brown-and-white-striped shell are seen breaking the water.

Quiet quickly returns as the sun sets and the sea darkens. The evening stars now appear and they seem to be reflected on the glassy sea below. But these reflections gradually blur, and they enlarge into luminous patches of light. Phosphorescent plankton are completing their evening rise to the surface. Their dim glows are all that will light the dark of this Paleozoic sea.

In the growing blackness, the image of the poison sea dims. The bioluminescent patches shrink and sharpen into yellow pinpoints of light. Far below, the electric lights of the Mohawk Valley are coming on, and now it is they that reflect the stars above. The poison sea is gone, long gone, just an image in the eye and mind of the pensive geologist.

Kaatskill Life, Summer 1994

REGRESSION TO THE MEAN

W E LIVE IN A WORLD where we are used to the idea of rising sea levels. During hurricane seasons, we expect to see the rising of the ocean's waters and the flooding of coastal landscapes. We may not be comfortable with the idea of coastal erosion, but we do see it as the "norm."

Few of us would recognize it, but this is a bias. We are comfortable with the notion of rising sea levels not because that actually is the norm, but because we live in a world where the climate has been warming up ever since the end of the Ice Age. As the climate has warmed up glaciers have melted and meltwater has poured into the seas, raising their levels worldwide.

There is, however, nothing actually inevitable about rising sea levels; it could be the other way around. Suppose that the climate was cooling down. Then ice would be forming, water would be withdrawn from the sea to make the ice and the sea levels of the world would be dropping. Throughout the length of Earth history it must be that there have been as many times of dropping sea level as there were risings. Neither is favored over the long term.

A rising sea level is often called a transgression while a falling sea level is called a regression. Transgressing seas do leave coastal regions susceptible to storm flooding and damage. Such coasts are prone to erosion and, in fact, do erode away.

Regressive coasts are quite different; as the sea levels drop, rivers bring sand and mud into the seas and pile them up. The coasts advance seaward. We call that progradation.

You and I are not likely to ever see a good regression, not unless there is a dramatic shift in the climate. So we will never see a whole coastline prograding. But we can go back in time to eras when the seas were retreating and see the results in the rocks. From Woodstock, travel east on the Glasco Pike to Mount Marion. There, where Plattekill Creek crosses the road, you will see a towering outcrop. It is mostly black shale. The rock was once black mud deposited in relatively deep waters of the Devonian seas, a little less than 400 million years ago.

The black shale is a fine grained deposit of mud. Mud accumulates in very thin sheets at the bottom of a quiet sea. The sea was quiet because of the great depths. There were no currents, or tides or waves in the deep water. But look upward; at the top of the exposure you will see a number of thick-bedded strata. If you could get up there, you would find that these are sandstones. Overall, the outcrop grades from shale to sandstone, from mud to sand. That's the regressive sequence.

What was happening? At this time the Acadian Mountains, located where the Berkshires are today, were actively rising in a dramatic and important mountain-building event called the Acadian Orogeny. As these mountains uplifted they began to weather and erode. Large masses of rock were converted into even larger volumes of mud, sand, and gravel. That's the fate of weathering rock. Mountain streams transported all of this material as sediment into the adjacent sea. That's us right here; Woodstock and the whole Hudson Valley region were under water. Marine currents sorted out all of the fine-grained mud and carried it far out to sea, where it settled to the bottom as the black mud that hardened into our black shale.

But as mountain building continued, gluts of coarse-grained sediment overwhelmed the mud and layers of sand began to pile up Thus, when this sediment hardened we ended up with the shale-to-sandstone sequence. That's a regression.

Go back westward on the Glasco Pike. You will soon encounter other outcrops. These are all composed of more sandstone. At the top of the hill, on the right, you will even see the cross section of an old river channel. The regression had succeeded; it had transformed a sea into a land area. There should be one of those New York State historical markers up there. It should say "Here the Woodstock area rose out of the sea." After all, that was a historical event!

Woodstock Times, June 1999

PART THREE

The Catskill Delta

"OVERLOOKING" ATLANTIS

IT WAS 2,300 YEARS AGO that Plato wrote of a great island, "larger than Libya and Asia taken together." His island was the fabled Atlantis, and it lay out in the Atlantic Ocean beyond the Straits of Gibraltar. The story went on: fully 9,000 years before Plato's time, Atlantis was a great city-state which controlled an empire extending as far east as Egypt and Italy. After fighting and losing a war with the Athenians, Atlantis was consumed by a day and a half of earthquakes and floods. The whole land mass sank into the ocean and has been lost ever since.

It's a wonderful story and just the type that we scientists love to debunk. But the word "debunk" implies ridicule, and when you ridicule a popular myth, you run the risk of appearing arrogant. Now, believe me, arrogance is not exactly unheard of in science, so let's take a careful look at the story of Atlantis. As is so often the case, the true story is a lot better than the myth.

You can start by climbing up the Overlook Mountain trail and gazing out eastward from the top of the Wall of Manitou, the Catskills' eastern escarpment. A lot of geologists have done this and nearly all have pondered the same question: Where did all this rock come from? Beneath the Overlook trail are many thousands of feet of sandstone. That's only part of what is sometimes called the "Appalachian Sequence." The whole sequence consists of sedimentary rocks about 40,000 thousand feet or so thick. It wasn't always rock, it was once all sediment. Sediment has to come from somewhere and 40,000 feet of it has to come from somewhere big, so you can appreciate the geological curiosity.

In the 1840s James Hall, the great Albany geologist, got very interested in finding where all that sand had come from. He traced these sediments all across North America and soon convinced himself that the thick Appalachian deposits always thinned to the west. It must be, he thought, that if the sediments thinned to the west, then they must have come from a source in the east. Now James Hall had no interests in the myth of Atlantis, but other geologists wondered about that source land. Was this the real Atlantis?

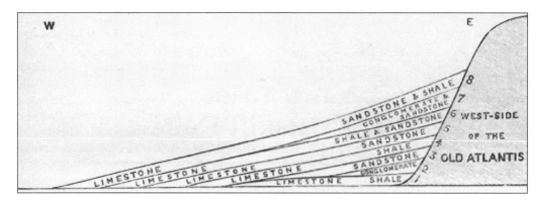

The Appalachian sediments thin to the west. (Author's collection)

In the late nineteenth century, Charles Callaway calculated the total volume of sediment that made up the Appalachian sequence. From this he estimated that there must have once been a source land about the size of Australia out in the North Atlantic. Callaway thought that the weathering and erosion of this source land provided the sediments of the Appalachian sequence and similar rocks in Europe. Callaway thought that he had come up with the scientific discovery of an ancient lost continent—a real one! He called it "Old Atlantis." Callaway's continent was about 350 million years older than Plato's.

Callaway's idea remained popular into the twentieth century, but it didn't hold up all that well as oceanographers learned more and more about the floor of the North Atlantic. Surely, if there had once been an Atlantis out there, then some remnant would remain, but none was ever found.

The solution to the source land problem came in the late 1960s and it was a terrific story, much greater than the old myth. Continents and oceans, it turned out were not eternal. Once there had been no Atlantic Ocean at all, neither was there a North America or Europe. Instead there were great land masses, ancestral to the ones that we are familiar with. Back then, an ancestral Europe was drifting westward and actively colliding with an earlier form of North America. As the two crushed together a great mountain range was up thrust all along the collision zone. Such things do happen and can even be seen today. India is colliding with Asia and the Himalayas are the product of that collision. Our 350-million-year-old ancestral Appalachians are called the Acadian Mountains and they, not Atlantis, provided the sediments we see today in places like Overlook Mountain.

So the Atlantis of Plato's myth never did exist. But when we debunk his story, it's not arrogance, but confidence that science can provide a better story which motivates us. Our story tells of moving and colliding continents. The story speaks of once towering mountain ranges which are no more. It's a good story and one of the most important scientific discoveries of this century. And to me, the best is that the story comes from the rocks.

So take a hike up Overlook and gaze east. Find the Berkshires on the distant horizon. That's Atlantis! Adds something to the view, doesn't it?

Woodstock Times, February 1997

MOVING MOUNTAINS

THE VIEW OF THE HUDSON VALLEY from along the Catskill Escarpment is one of the great sights of the East. You can enjoy it anywhere along a ten-mile stretch from Overlook Mountain to North Point, but the most famous vantage point is long gone. That was the 130-foot-long piazza of the old Catskill Mountain House Hotel. A seventy-mile stretch of the Hudson lowlands lay visible below the hotel site. On certain days, when the clarity and humidity are just right, the atmosphere becomes a magnifying glass and that view can overwhelm you.

Mountain House guests commonly arose just before sunrise. With a little luck they got a special treat. The cool morning fogs would enshroud the valley below. Then the sun would slowly rise above the clouds, illuminating them brightly from above. It's still a sight to see.

Beautiful as it is, this view thwarted the efforts of artists to capture it. Seventy miles is just too much to put on a canvas and anything less just won't do. Only Frederic Church solved the problem. In his *Sunrise in the Catskills*, he painted the view at dawn. He showed the sun rising above a valley filled with clouds. That left all these unpaintable seventy miles of valley floor to the imagination of the viewer. It worked; the painting is a gem!

The twentieth century brought something new to the view. With electricity, the nighttime valley has gradually lit up. On a clear, dry, moonless night with the starry sky above and the lights below the view is a sight to behold.

The hotel is long gone, but the view remains. The Mountain House site remains a popular goal for the hikers and picnickers of North/South Lake State Park. It's a popular site for visiting geologists as well. My colleagues and I come to see the view just like anyone else. But we get to see two views at North Lake: one of the landscape as it is, and one as it was during the Devonian age. To the far east is the low profile of the Taconic Mountains. These humble mountains are the erosional remnants of older and very larger mountains. They are the roots of the old Acadian Mountains.

Out there, between 350 and 400 million years ago, a great mountain-building event took place. If you had sat on the Mountain House piazza for those fifty million years, then the mountains would have risen before your very eyes. It was one of the biggest such events to ever occur in eastern North America. At their greatest, these peaks, called the Acadian Mountains, stood perhaps 30,000 feet above sea level.

As I look east from the hotel piazza, I can still see those old mountains. The jagged peaks are snow capped. It's a tropical climate here 350 million years ago, so only the highest slopes are white. Below the snow the mountains are a uniform smoky blue. There is enough haze so that the details of the landscape are not clear, but you can see many deeply cut gullies in the upper mountain slopes. It's common for heavy rains to activate the gullies, which then tear into the upper mountain slopes. Farther downslope the gullies merge into very substantial and extremely jagged canyons. During rainy times, great cataracts of water plummet down these valleys. The waters are brown with freshly eroded sediment; there is no flood or erosion control in the Devonian.

Toward the base of the mountain range the canyons empty out onto great heaps of sediment. These are beautiful; they have been sculpted into gently sloping fans and the light-colored sedi-

The piazza at the Catskill Mountain House. (Author's collection)

ments shine brightly in the sun. There is no foliage to cover these fresh sediments.

But there is foliage farther below. In front of the fans is an enormous landscape of swamps, shallow ponds, and many streams. It's a huge delta complex, which geologists have come to call the Catskill Delta. The delta is teeming with life, mostly primitive plants. There is an irony here. In looking at this ancient delta environment I am looking at the Catskills of today. That's because, with time, the sediments of that ancient Catskill Delta spread out into today's New York State. They hardened into rock and are now the sedimentary rocks of the Catskills of today. In the great cycles of time one landscape is the parent of another.

And so it is that I sit upon the porch of a long-gone hotel and gaze at mountains which eroded away 300 million years ago. Such are the moments in the life of the geologist.

Woodstock Times, October 1996

A NIGHT ON OVERLOOK MOUNTAIN

THE ROAD TO OVERLOOK MOUNTAIN used to be important. It served two main functions: it brought resort tourists up to the mountain's hotels. Several were built there in succession; they all burned. Also it brought downhill lumbering wagons loaded with Catskill bluestone from the area quarries. Today the road is no longer important. It can't even be called a road anymore; it is just a hiking trail.

The trip to the top of Overlook is well worth the effort as the peak offers one of the best views in all of the Catskills. To visit this mountain in the early fall, just as the leaves are turning, and to spend the night there under a rising full moon is one of the great experiences of our Catskills. The climb up the path is a bit tedious, however. The trail has none of the interesting steep, rocky stretches that you usually encounter on Catskill trails, just a steady, grinding incline. You know that the long climb is nearly over when you reach the old walls of the last of the Overlook Mountain House hotels. The ruin is a gem. Four stories tall and composed of poured cement, it has the look of something that will be there for an eternity. It won't.

Beyond the hotel is the mountaintop itself and a state fire tower with its panoramic view. The peak is windswept, and large knobs of rock poke through the thin soils. The strata speak to the geologist and tell of the ancient Acadian Mountains, which once lay to the east, but are now nearly entirely eroded away. The rocks we see here were once coarse sands, sediment which accumulated on the slopes of those long-ago mountains. These are not sediments anymore; time has hardened them into rock.

Sunset is subtle: The afternoon light dims imperceptibly and then the sky darkens rapidly. This location has been here for four-and-one-half billion years and the site has witnessed all of the sunsets that such a length of time brings. To the east, exactly as the sun descends, a full moon rises; it is the fabled harvest moon. The first lights to join the moon are the brightest stars; they are soon joined by the lesser lights of the full moon's sky.

I will have no fire at this night's camp. I would enjoy the heat, as it is no longer warm out. I wish instead to be alone in time here, and I do not want any bright lights to distract me from participating in this particular cycle of time.

Off to the east are the Taconic and Berkshire Mountains. These beautiful and serene hills are the remnants of the much older Acadian Mountains, which once

The view from the top of Overlook. (Titus)

towered over this horizon. It grows fully dark now and those hilly landscapes stand in sharp contrast under the rising moonlight. As the moon continues its ascent, it draws away from the mountains, and they fade into the darkness. With an evening mist, the lights of civilization in the valley below also disappear.

The New England mountains were not always here, but it has now been over 350 million years that the moon has been rising above their silhouettes. Before then, the view was not that of New England but of an ancient ocean, the Iapetus Sea, unblemished by any land masses, let alone mountains. Back then, it must have seemed as if that sea's stretch extended forever into the east. But that was false, and there were clues of something going on out there beyond the eastern horizon. From time to time, dark clouds of smoke rose above the horizon. First they were only low, dim and distant, but later they appeared larger and darker than ever before. There had to have been a day, a moment in time, when a single pinnacle of land first emerged upon that horizon. During the lifetime of any Devonian age creature, no change would have been noticed, but as many life-times passed, that pinnacle was transformed from an occasional glimpse to a permanent fixture upon the seascape, growing larger and broader. Occasionally great, thunderous roars would emanate from that eastern monolith, and some-times even lightning could be seen within the billowing black masses of soot. It was the nighttime and moonlit eruptions that were the most spectacular. The

The ruins of the Overlook Mountain House. (Titus)

immense, rising clouds of dense smoke, sharply outlined in moonlight, would have been unforgettable—had anyone been there to remember.

In between these, more and more frequent volcanic episodes, the peaks of the now great mountain range became white with snow. Even here in the tropics they had grown tall enough. Beneath the snowy fringe, the mountains were a desolate brown and lifeless gray. But as they loomed taller and closer, a thin low red horizon competed with those elevated, but more somber, colors. Then, finally joining the red, was a very low wisp of green.

The Overlook Mountain vicinity had once gazed out upon the unbroken blue of the Iapetus Sea, but now it would witness the disappearance of that sea. The red and green horizon grew closer and the image sharpened into that of a low tropical foliage growing upon the brick-red soils of a coastal delta. These were the world's most primitive forests, dominated by the by the world's most primitive trees. Crawling the soils were the first land animals, primitive insects, millipedes and spiders. These were the pioneers of forest ecology, and forest ecology is the chief claim to fame of the great Catskill Delta.

The delta advanced slowly, but it could not be stopped; time cannot be stopped. The waters went from salt to fresh; they suddenly grew murky and brown, and the Overlook vicinity was buried. The shrouds of burial were the sediments of the rivers, lakes and swamps of the great delta. These soft, warm sediments encased and preserved much of the delta forests.

Millions of years, then tens of millions of years of blackness followed. The pressure of the thickening sediment intensified. The great delta became a petrifaction, its soft warm sediments hardened into cold stone sculptures of rivers, lakes, marshes, and forests. After about one hundred and fifty million years of increasing pressure, the weight of the overburden stopped growing. And, after a long pause, the pressure, ever so slowly, began to lessen.

If it was possible for light to penetrate rock, even a little, then, over the next 200 million years the Overlook vicinity would have become dimly and then brightly illuminated. But this does not happen; light does not pass through rock and Overlook lay, for all of this time, in complete blackness.

The sleep of Overlook was dreamless and darker than anything humans can know. It was deepest and coldest just before the dawn. Above there were thick and heavy glaciers grinding their way southward. The full moon, now low in the western sky, brightly illuminated a plain of arctic desolation extending, in all directions, as far as could be seen. Only in the west were there peaks that rose above this crystalline sea. These appeared as silhouettes of black against the radiant moonlit horizon.

The processes of weathering and erosion do their work slowly but they never quit. Glaciers do speed up the process and the inevitable results are sudden: the breakthrough occurred and sunlight, for the first time in 350 million years, warmed the strata of Overlook.

* * *

Just exactly as the harvest moon sinks beneath the horizon, the new day's sun breaks above the cloud banks of the Hudson below. This view, a Frederic Church masterpiece, has returned once again as it has for millions of years, and as it will for millions more.

I sleepily watch the sunrise above the low fogs of the Hudson Valley. Beyond there is neither an Iapetus Sea nor an Acadian Mountain Range to be seen, only the low blue hills of the Berkshires. I am stiff and cold and in need of coffee. That can be found in the lowlands below, where I will soon return.

Time, the English geologist James Hutton observed, gives us no vestige of a beginning, no prospect of an end.

Kaatskill Life, Fall 1994

NAME THAT TOMB

PRATTSVILLE, along the banks of the Schoharie River, is steeped in Catskill history. It's emblematic of the some of the most progressive aspects of the area's history, and at the same time, it represents many of the mistakes people made as our region developed. Zadock Pratt was the towering, overwhelming personality in the town's development. Even today, his influences permeate the village.

Pratt was a founder of the Catskill tanning industry. From 1833 to 1846 his Prattsville tanneries turned out shoe leather for the New York City market. His tanneries, however, were dependent upon the bark of the hemlock tree, and when they were all cut down, the industry closed. We frown upon the wanton destruction of the Catskill hemlocks that characterized the nineteenth century, but our collective wisdom is based upon a history of trial and error. It was men such as Pratt who provided the errors.

But Pratt is also remembered for progressive attitudes toward urban planning. His Prattsville was a pioneering model in that field. Pratt laid out the streets, built the Greek Revival homes and planted the 1,000 trees that lined the village streets. Pratt founded churches and the town's academy as well. Prattsville today is still truly Pratt's town.

Zadock Pratt was a great man, but I suspect that history might have mostly forgotten him except for the one singular act of vanity that he was responsible for. Pratt, the Rameses II of the Schoharie, is remembered for Pratt Rock, his would-be tomb.

Pratt Rock consists of a series of stone carvings on a glacially plucked cliff along Route 23, just east of town and overlooking the old Pratt farm. The site is now a town park and open to visitors. You can hike the winding path up the steep slope toward the main carvings. If you tire along the way, you can sit upon stone seats thoughtfully carved into the mountain. The main level of carvings displays images and symbols of his life. There are carvings of the hemlock tree, a horse which hauled the bark to the tanneries, a strong arm to do the work and other emblems of the great man's life. There is a bust of Pratt himself and a poignant carving of his only son who died in the Civil War. Then there is the Pratt burial chamber itself.

Pratt's would-be burial chamber, bottom, and the stream channel just above it. (Titus)

Unlike the pharaohs, Pratt was never buried in the grotto carved out for him. One story is that the chamber was unsuitable for burial as it leaked water when it rained. The chamber is still there, and when I looked it over, I found that there may be some truth to that tale, along with a good geological story about Pratt Rock.

Pratt Rock is carved into sedimentary strata from the old Catskill Delta. Deposited nearly 400 million years ago, the sediments here record the coastal regions of a delta similar to that of the Mississippi River today. This was once the coastline of the old Catskill Sea. Rivers flowed across this location and poured their waters into the old ocean.

There is a lot of history here. I had little trouble finding bits and pieces of the old fossil Gilboa Forest, and I could picture its foliage along the old stream banks. But the most interesting horizons I found were those at the burial chamber itself. The ceiling of the chamber is made up of inclined strata. This horizon of rock formed on the sloping floor of an old stream channel. The beds slope down to the right, on what was once one side of a river, and farther along the outcrop they rise up again on the other shore. When I looked at the chamber ceiling, I found a horizon rich in a hash of broken plant remains. This stratum is likely very porous, and it's quite possible that this accounts for the leakage that caused the burial project to be abandoned. The pharaohs of arid Egypt faced no such problem.

And so this is one of the many ironies of geology. The great Zadock Pratt is buried in a nearby graveyard with all the other common folk of old Prattsville. That may be because about 370 million years ago some small river made a wrong turn. It's not Pratt buried in Pratt's tomb, but the sands of an ancient river!

Woodstock Times, October 1996

MEMORIES COME FLOODING BACK

A LITTLE EAST OF THE VILLAGE OF DELHI, I found a ledge of Devonian aged river sandstone that had been a deep channel cut into a now-fossil soil horizon. This sort of thing is hardly rare in the Catskills, there are, for example, many such fossil rivers in the hills above Woodstock, but this was a very good one, however, and it made me ponder the history that such ledges represent—there was a story here.

March 14th, 375,469,184 BC, late afternoon - All day long, very moist air has been rising up the slopes of the Acadian Mountains to the east, and now dark banks of storm clouds tower above the tall mountain peaks. Soon three closely spaced lines of thunderstorms unload, in quick succession, upon the mountains. The rain of the first line of storms quickly waterlogs the soils, and the subsequent torrents have raced off downhill in deep, fast-flowing, erosive streams. Deep gullies have been rapidly cut into the soft, blue-black earths of the upper mountain slopes. A thick ooze of dirty water (in fact, almost watery dirt) has funneled into gullies too numerous to count. Downslope, those gullies combine into several powerful cascading streams; deep channels are being widened rapidly. More dark earth is engulfed by the expanding flow, and whole slopes slide into the torrents. The rush of the confined water is being pushed and hurried along by the great flows

The deep channel deposit. (Titus)

backed up behind them.

From various compass points, similar ravines combine to a point well down on the face of the Acadians. Here, today's cascade has combined with many earlier ones like it to carve a great, vee-shaped cleft in the mountain range. This gap dwarfs the canyons above it. Through this cleft, on this day, flow several large

Niagaras; this is a catastrophic event, a thousand-year flood.

Below the narrows, the Acadian slopes level out. Vast piles of coarse sand and gravel have formed an enormous, rounded apron of sediment, draped against the slopes of the range. As it flows across this slope, the water breaks up into a number of smaller streams, which continue several miles down the gentle slope until the streams enter a broad plain, a flat morass of flooded bayous, marshes, and ponds.

The morass I speak of makes up the great Catskill Delta. Now, its various glutted and disorganized channels reflect the brunt of the flood; their powerful currents cut into adjacent floodplains and carve new channels. Their banks give way, and along with whole stands of trees, collapse into the flow. The channels are soon clogged and dammed with mud and broken trees. The dammed, blue-black waters rise up and flood out across the delta plain.

Flash floods like this are violent, but they don't last long. At the bottom of the now-submerged stream channels, the flood currents eventually slow down and the sediments begin to be deposited as dark horizons of muddy sand. Many plants and animals are being buried within these sands.

As the evening advances, the main flow continues down the channels of the delta. Downstream, the flow is still rapid, but it is beginning to ebb. At the mouths of the rivers, the flood waters, dark with sand and silt, are being disgorged into the Catskill Sea, which lies to the west. From above, large plumes of dirty water can be seen slowly expanding out into the sea. Many tree trunks and a flotsam of broken foliage drift seaward, half hidden in the darkening skies.

By midnight the storms have long been over. The sky is clear and the stars shine, competing with a wine-colored moon. The upper slopes of the Acadian Mountains are now dark, silent silhouettes. Downstream, the churning flows of the day are still rapid and gurgling with noise, but the normal languid flow of the delta will soon return. The rivers are still dirty, but they are clearing. Offshore the plumes of sediment are settling into thick strata of sticky sand. A large number of shellfish are dying in that burial. Their shells will lie, buried as fossils, for 375 million years.

It has been a very hard day for the biota of the Catskill Delta. But nobody cares. The world of the Devonian is a soul-less one; there is no mourning, no grief, no pity or even self pity. Indeed, there is no real understanding of exactly what happened today, and by midnight, there are few living creatures who can even remember these terrible events.

Woodstock Times, July 1998

SILENCE OF THE LIMBS

IT'S NOVEMBER, and the hiking season is pretty much over. There are still a few relatively mild days, but there are so many fewer reasons to get out now. The foliage with its green is gone, and the landscape is for the most part just a dull gray. Darkness comes so early now. Later the snow may draw some of us out on skis or snowshoes, but that is yet to come. For the time being, the scenery is uninspiring.

But I have found one outdoors' experience that is pretty much confined to this time of year, and it is something that does sometimes draw me out for one last end-of-the-season Catskill hike. It's not something that I can go and see, nor something that I can hear or feel. Instead it is the very silence of the woods at this time of year.

Each November brings a few days when the skies are a uniform gray, and the gloomy weather patterns seem to settle into complete doldrums. Pick one of those days and hike high up into the Catskills so that you are far away from any road noise. There are often no planes above our mountains, but if there are any, just wait until they have passed by. Pick a good spot and sit and listen. Not a breath of air stirs, and even if it did a little, there are no leaves to rustle at this time of the year. Once in a while a twig or limb will fall, but these events are scarce and momentary. The forest becomes so completely silent that it is almost unnerving.

In this season of the year, there are few animals stirring. The insects are seasonal, and this year's generation has all died; the next generation sleeps in its egg cases, silently awaiting the spring thaws. The song birds have departed, and most of the ground animals have settled into some burrow for the winter. In short it is mighty quiet up in the mountains at this time of year.

To a geologist there is a special experience here. Silence is unusual in our world, but that is only *our* world that I am talking about. Today we expect the woods to be noisy with insects, birds and furry animals, but that has not always been the case. Long ago these noise-making creatures did not exist. I am thinking of the Gilboa Forest which long ago presided over our Catskill landscape.

The Gilboa Forest was a very different sort of woods. There were no mammals, neither were there birds. There were insects, but they were so primitive that they had not yet evolved the ability to make noise. Noise making is something we take for granted, and probably regard mostly as a nuisance. But we should not forget that it is a relatively complex form of animal behavior and that was something far beyond the abilities of Gilboa's primitive creatures.

Neither were the trees of Gilboa very noisy. They lacked true leaves, and so it is not likely that they would have been able to make much of a rustle. Even on a windy day, the forest of Gilboa must have been a remarkably quiet place. All this silence ended, maybe 300 million years ago, when more advanced insects appeared and began their songs. Eventually birds and other animals followed suit and the world's forests and jungles became noisy.

So that is what draws me into the mountain at this time of year. It's a chance to go and experience a form of nature that has been gone for all those 300 million years. I like the western slopes of Hunter Mountain. These face the interior of the Catskills and are shielded from the cacophony of the Hudson Valley. Near Woodstock I would hike up to the Overlook trail and turn down the yellow trail to Echo Lake. On a really quiet day, the lake's name truly should be a misnomer. Try it; it's any year's one last good excuse for a hike into the mountains.

Woodstock Times, November 1996

WHAT KATY DID

DURING THE NINETEENTH CENTURY, Plattekill Clove, like much of the Catskills, developed an economy based on bluestone, timber, and tourist hotels. Now, much of it has returned to wilderness, and the old forest ecology struggles back to normal. It's nice. I have been, off and on, occupying the little red cabin at the top of the clove, courtesy of the Catskill Center for Conservation and Development. It is my habit to walk the clove road late at night just to be out. I recently started my walk on a dark, humid, moonless night, one that was fragrant with high summer. I wouldn't see much, but I would listen. What I would hear was the past, and not just the recent past.

The forest at the top of the clove was surprisingly quiet. A few nondescript insects and late-night birds sang in the trees, but there really weren't many of them. There were other creatures, however. In the distance, from Plattekill Mountain across the clove, a lone "ARROOOOO" broke the quiet, and it was followed by another and then a cacophony of howls. It was a pack of coyotes. I have no idea what they were saying, but it was a grand thing to hear. It's an ancient wilderness sound; ancestral dogs first evolved about fifty million years ago at a time called the Eocene Epoch. The old road had brought me a first journey into the past, but it was only a short trip compared to what was to come.

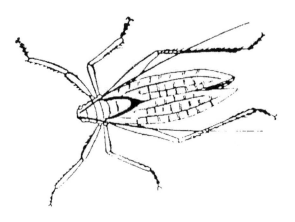

A katydid. (author's collection)

As I continued down the Platte Clove Road, I passed a dark meadow. There was a different sound there. I have no idea what type of bug it was, but there was a steady insect noise, not a hum but more of a steady wheezing sound. It was a signal that I was entering into the ancient, nocturnal domain of the insects. Down the road I soon passed under a dark, gloomy canopy of trees. A handful of lightning bugs were still out, but the dark branches above me belonged to the katydids. They chirped loudly, all were competing for the attentions of prospective mates. Their combined calls created a cacophony of "KATY DID, KATY DID, KATY DID." Some abbreviated their calls to a quicker "SHE DID, SHE DID, SHE DID." These were not gossips, just individuals driven by a Darwinian drive to reproduce. This was not music or even musical, but the richness of the sounds on a warm summer night was intoxicating.

Farther down the hill, I reached a more open roadway. Below me, I could see the Hudson Valley out beyond the Clove. Lights in the valley glittered, but up here it was nearly all darkness. There were a few flashes of lightning from a storm, very far to the north. The highlander katydids had faded into the trees behind me, and they had been replaced by a new sound from the brush below, it was the sound of the lowland crickets. This was a different call, but it had the same Darwinian motive. Crickets are far more melodic and more communal in their calls. They seem to coordinate their chirps. As you walk along you will hear one chirping away. But soon the call from one side of the road will grade, with the same tone and tempo, into the sound of another cricket on the other side of the road. It is as if you had passed from one stereo speaker to another. Why do Katydid's compete and why do crickets sing in harmony? I am a geologist, and I don't know such things, but I do know that both strategies will succeed and next year there will be a new generation of katydids and crickets.

Generations of these singing insects have been around a long time. They appeared probably about 300 million years ago, during the Carboniferous Period, and they have been an enormous success ever since. The sounds I was listening to had already been ancient by the time the first dinosaurs heard them. And these sounds, though not eternal, will likely be heard for hundreds of millions of years to come.

I continued my downhill nighttime solitude. In the distant valley below, I could see the lights of the Kingston-Rhinebeck Bridge. I soon reached the hairpin curve in the road and sat upon one of the large boulders placed there to keep cars from careening into the canyon. I surveyed Platte Clove in its darkness. There were still occasional flashes of lightning, and that storm even managed a little breeze, though it was too distant to bother me. I sat and listened, mostly in vain, for more sounds. What I had heard was the return of the wilderness in the reforested Catskills. These noisy creatures had been here for hundreds of millions of years. Then they were gone when man cut down the trees and now they are back. Their calls are from geological time itself, and I had listened. Near me were a few empty beer bottles and a little pile of cigarette butts; I was not the first to sit here. Others come for other reasons.

Woodstock Times, September 1999

MONSTER IN THE CLOSET

I DON'T KNOW WHAT IT IS ABOUT MARCH, but I seem to start finding silverfish around the house, especially in my clothes closet. What attracts them? I don't know; they are just bugs, who can explain them? I usually pay little attention to such things, but this year there was something about them that caught my eye. I am supposed to be a scientist, and we scientists are supposed to be curious about such things, so I looked them up, and it was worth the effort.

It turns our silverfish are not just run of the mill "bugs." They are, in fact, something quite special and of particular interest to a paleontologist. So, if you are having a problem with silverfish, do what I did. Stop for a moment and take a good look at them. Now that will be tough to do, as they love to scurry around quickly and don't care to stop to be looked at. I recommend some bug spray; after all, it is the interest of science (and a bug-free home). Anyway, once you get one to stop moving, you will quickly see that they are not like other insects. You won't have to know much entomology to tell silverfish are very primitive insects; they just look it. They do have six legs, as all good insects should, but that is about it.

Silverfish belong to a very ancient group of insects. Most insects have wings, four wings in fact, but silverfish have none at all. Nor did any of their ancestors; the lineage extends back to a time before insects had evolved wings. And when I say "extends back": I mean a *long, long* time; silverfish date back to the Devonian time period. Around here, that is of some significance, as all of the local bedrock is Devonian in age.

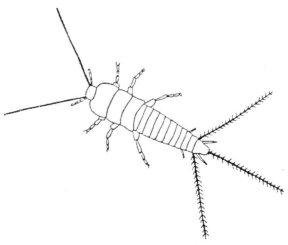

A silverfish. (Author's collection)

In fact, all of the sedimentary rocks of the Catskills were deposited during the Devonian, and as luck would have it, most of those sediments accumulated in a terrestrial setting, one where insects abounded. This was the Gilboa Forest of the Catskill delta complex. The land of Gilboa was, like any very large delta, a morass of forests, lakes, ponds, swamps, and rivers. Its climate was tropical, and it must have had a lush ecology, perfect for insects. And it is rich in fossils, sometimes including insects not terribly different from our silverfish. Those silverfish, or at least their ancestors, are among the earliest inhabitants of what would eventually become our Catskills and that's something for us to take pride in.

Creatures such as silverfish have a special place in the hearts of paleontologist. We call them "living fossils," and that's a good term. They have evolved so slowly and so very little that they remained virtually unchanged from their ancestors of hundreds of millions of years ago. Living fossils are like keyholes to the past. We can look at them and see creatures as they were in the distant geological times.

So why were these monsters from the past so common in my closet? It turns out they love starch, and starch is abundant in paper. I looked back the closet and, sure enough, there were several old copies of *Woodstock Times*. It would seem that newspaper is not just food for the mind.

Woodstock Times, March 1999

A NIGHT TO REMEMBER

ONEONTA, August 15, 382,439,953 BC, the predawn hours—There is, of course, no Oneonta at this time, but the land is here. It is a morass of bayous and swamps, populated by the primitive trees of the Gilboa Forest. It's the end of a moonless night, and it's still dark out, but there is a growing light and it's not the approaching sun. Over the past several weeks there has been a slow-moving pinpoint of light in the nighttime sky. It is an asteroid, about a half mile across. It's moving in from the south, and as it enters the thin upper atmosphere, it is starting to glow quite brightly. Its speed is about twenty miles per second, but it is still so far away that it seems to hang in the sky. As it comes closer, however, its apparent motion speeds up. Now as it enters the denser parts of the Earth's atmosphere, friction heats it into a great flare. The whole eastern sky lights up, silhouetting the black horizon below.

This is the critical moment; if the asteroid is small enough, and its angle of approach low enough, then it will bounce off the atmosphere and skip harmlessly back into space. If not . . . The flare's flight path doesn't skip, it plummets silently and disappears behind the southern horizon.

Moments pass in what seems to be an endless pause, and then comes a great and instantaneous shock of light. It flickers for a few seconds, and then the whole southeast horizon glows red. The color brightens to an orange, then a yellow, and finally a brilliant radiance of white. An enormous gassy fireball rises rapidly above the horizon, followed by a mass of black smoke.

Incredibly, this entire scene has been played out during thirty seconds of complete silence, but that ends abruptly. The nearby ground begins to hiss and then roar. Great waves of earth radiate across the landscape. They are powerful surface earthquake waves that look and move very much like the waves of an ocean. As they pass by, geysers of watery sand erupt from the ground. All of the trees fall down; their primitive roots are unable to support them on the shaking, soft, wet ground.

In another twenty seconds, the great shock wave of the impact blast itself hits Oneonta. For several minutes the landscape rocks with the combined effect of the earthquake and the atmospheric shock waves. Then, at four minutes after the impact, the actual sound of the asteroid's impact catches up with the chaos. Only the word "unimaginable" does any justice to the power that this sound signals.

Meanwhile, that fireball has blown a hole in the stratosphere and it continues to rise. It's a hundred miles high now and the trailing plume of dust below is catching the high sunlight of the still-approaching dawn. The whole thing has become an incredible pillar of white, starkly outlined by the surrounding dark. The pillar is a chimney with walls of dust; its flue is a vacuum which is drawing a vast draft of air upward. Back at Oneonta things had quieted momentarily, but now a new breeze has started, and it's being sucked toward the chimney. It quickly speeds up to gale force and then to hurricane speeds. All this air is drawn up the chimney and vented out into space.

Next comes a hailstorm of dust and rocks. This is the debris that the impact blasted out of the earth and threw tens of thousands of feet up. Now it's all falling back again. The first rocks plop loudly into the still churning mud. Then the higher-flying rocks start returning as an incredibly dense shower of fiery meteors. Hundreds of them cascade out of the sky, and they light up the entire landscape.

In the east, the sun is about to rise, but it's a futile effort; sunlight won't fall again upon Oneonta for months. A great stratospheric shroud of black has been expanding ominously from the south. Along its front an enormous and continuous rage of dry lightning forms an expanding plexus of sparkles that illuminate the wrecked landscape below. Gradually, a moonless, starless black engulfs the area.

But if there is nothing to see, there is still plenty to hear and feel. The winds still howl and more rocks continue to fall out of the sky. And the temperature has been rising alarmingly over the past hour; it is already more than 100 degrees and getting hotter. Once again light penetrates the dusty gloom, but only in the form of burning plant debris falling slowly out of the sooty black sky. To the south, closer to the impact, forests have been ignited and their burning embers have been lofted into the sky. It is a hellish sight.

Kaatskill Life, Fall 1997

PART FOUR
Environmental Geology

ERODING VALUES

A S A PALEONTOLOGIST, I do not have to face very many serious environmental issues. None of the fossil species I deal with are endangered; none of
the environments I study are threatened. They all disappeared by about 350 million years ago. As a writer about geology, things are a bit different. It's only natural for a geologist to take a very long-term view of things, and so it has been that,
in traveling about in the Catskills, I do sometimes come across some developing
problems. And, surprisingly, that includes the Catskill Park, the forever wild preserve that the state began to put aside more than a hundred years ago.

Not surprisingly, the forest preserve attracts people who, for the most part,
have a real sense of the value of this land. Very few would deliberately do harm
to this landscape. The trouble is that there are so very many of us. We can overwhelm a landscape without meaning to. The most serious example is at
Kaaterskill Falls. The site is blessed with wonderful scenery and cursed by the
many thousands of visitors who come every year to see it. The best approach to
the falls is to take the yellow trail up from Bastion Falls below. Nobody intends to
do harm and nobody does much harm, but the traffic is so heavy that the wear
and tear on the Bastion Falls trail has really been showing for quite a while now,
and it's getting much worse. The path is just plain beat up.

It may be worse from above. Many people choose to descend into the clove
from the top of the falls. This takes them down a very steep, and erosion-prone,
slope. People tend to slip and slide as they struggle down the steep clay surface.
The damage has been very bad there. Again, it's not anybody's fault, it's a collective and cumulative effect.

There's a conflict of values here. The land is owned by the people and open to
the public. The New York State Constitution guarantees that all of us can walk
anywhere we want to in the forest preserve. Nobody has the right to tell you or
me where we can or can't go. Such restrictions could never be enforced anyway.

Kaaterskill Falls. (Titus)

But, in exercising our rights, we harm the very land that we have chosen to save. In fact, throughout almost all of the preserve the damage has been minimal, and human nature being what it is, almost none of us take responsibility for the very little bit of damage that each of us does.

Few of us can see into the long term future and appreciate the damage that is underway. But a geologist can, and there are areas where the damage has gotten so bad that something must be done. Inevitably, other locations will share the same fate. It's best we develop strategies now so we can deal with these problems as they become manifest.

This gets us back to Kaaterskill Falls which is certainly the place to start. The state has put up signs asking people to be careful, but that is unlikely to be of much help. After all, it's not *me* who is the problem; it's all of those other people. An obvious approach is to build a wooden staircase. Back in the hotel days there was one here, and tourists had an easy time of it, visiting the falls. But this is a nature preserve and, in theory, we are not supposed to be building unnatural things here.

That's the kind of problem all preserves eventually must face. We have to choose, and I'm afraid the choice is forced upon us. We can't have a perfect preserve and allow everyone to enjoy it at the same time without a few compromises. I do hope that the day will soon come when a staircase at Kaaterskill Falls will allow people to visit the site while minimizing the damage. There is some precedent. There is a fine wooden staircase at Mine Kill Falls and it's a nice looking one. That site is not suffering the kind of damage we lament at Kaaterskill Falls.

EDITORIAL NOTE: Erosion continues unabated at Kaaterskill Falls nearly ten years after this article was published.

Woodstock Times, April 1998

THE FLOODS OF OLD ORLEANS

I HAD BEEN TO THE OUTCROP BEFORE. It is one of those classic geological sites in the Catskills. It's just a tenth of a mile up Route 23 from the Cornwallville scenic-view parking lot. You hike up the road, cross it and there are the rocks. The exposure displays the cross-sectional view of a Devonian-age river perhaps 385 million or so years old. This is typical deposit of the ancient Catskill Delta. I had been there many times, but this visit was different. I came here not so much to see the rocks but to gain some wisdom.

The Route 23 river channel outcrop. (Titus)

I climbed up to the river channel itself. It was 11:17 AM, November 3rd, 2005 AD. I put a finger on the wall of rock. These sandstones had once been sand and that sand had been deposited in the old river channel. Before, there had been rock, and before the rock had been sand, this space had been water; a river current had once flowed through here. I looked into the rock, and it was as if it was transparent. I could see into the old river and feel its current; the flow was strong and it came from behind me. I felt swept forward by the water, as if carried into the past.

From in front of me the creature approached. It was a very primitive fish; they are called placoderms. They were characterized by heavy bony armor; it made these fish a bit sluggish, but they were still strong enough swimmers. They had strong jaws, but curiously no teeth. Instead their jaw bones were exposed as sharp meat cleaver-like structures. They were quite capable of tearing up any prey or any foe. These were not fish to be messed around with; I was looking at the top of the Devonian food pyramid.

The fish approached me, but the animal was now struggling with that current. The river was reaching toward flood stage, and the currents were getting a bit much for a placoderm. The animal struggled and managed to swim forward far enough so that, just for a moment, its nose could just touch where I had placed my finger. Then the current picked up, and the fish gave up; it drifted backwards, accepting the powerful flow. This was at 11:18 on November 3rd, 384,232,005 BC.

Briefly that fish and I had shared the same space but we would never share the same moment. I was on one side of a wall, and he was on the other side of time. But in my mind's eye I could see that other time. It beckoned me on. I turned to my right and climbed up to the top of the riverbank. Beyond the bank was a low swampy area. This was just one of many ancient, Devonian-age landscapes and nobody bothers putting names on any of them. But maybe it's time. I decided to call the land beyond the river "Old Orleans." That river needed a name too; it should be the "Little Mississippi."

Like the modern Mississippi River, this one crossed a great delta. The Mississippi Delta is one of our Earth's largest. It is the product of millions of years of sediment being carried down "Old Man River" and left in a growing heap of earth that we call Louisiana. Likewise, the Devonian's Little Mississippi River once crossed the Catskill Delta. It must have been just as large as any modern delta. That's big, and today all of the Catskills are essentially a petrifaction of its old delta sands. I stepped back and looked at the profile of the mountains above me. I looked at mountains and saw a once great delta.

Deltas had, of course, recently been in the news. Like so many others I had watched as the hurricanes swept the Gulf Coast and had seen the nearly complete destruction that had followed. It was, with that in mind, that I now sought wisdom from the rocky oracles in front of me. I looked again; beyond the banks of the Little Mississippi, reddish brown flood waters were gushing over the riverbank and spreading across that swampy land. Old Orleans was being flooded. This was not very difficult; Old Orleans, like the modern version, lay just about at sea level. Soon, as far as I could see, the landscape was drowning. I climbed back down off the outcrop.

I traveled up the road about four-tenths of a mile. There, in the year 2005, was a towering cliff of rock. It was a magnificent outcrop, something geologists love to explore. There were a hundred feet or so of stratified rock exposed here. The first seventy displayed a sequence of red shales, alternating with meter-thick horizons of gray sandstone.

I examined those sandstones and saw that they were very well laminated. These were flood deposits. I looked up and counted about a half dozen of them. The shale beds lay in between the flood deposits. I looked at these and saw that many, maybe all of them, had been the sediments of delta plain. Some of them showed clear signs of soil forming processes. Soil chemistry had turned them to blotchy grays and greens.

The rocks were speaking to me, and they were telling stories about many rainy seasons of the distant Devonian past. The Catskill Delta lay in a monsoon climate. Each summer the heat of the delta plain grew intense. Great billowing masses of hot air rose above the delta like the hot air balloons. As hot air rose, it left something of a vacuum behind. To replace what was rising, more air was drawn in off of the Catskill Sea to the west. That air was humid and, and it was this air that heated up and rose. Soon the rising humid air was cooled. Cooling air

A towering outcrop along Route 23. *Opposite, top:* A fossil soil,
notice the light colored horizon. *Bottom:* Mud cracks. (Titus)

loses it ability to hold water vapor. Something had to give, and the results were torrents of heavy rainfall all across the delta. With such rainfall, periods of great flooding are inevitable and those floods washed vast quantities of sand out of the mountains to the east in today's New England. I was looking at an outcropping of rocks on Route 23, but I was seeing monsoons!

There was more, if there are rainy seasons there must also be dry seasons. I would find the evidence for that soon enough. There was a large boulder at the base of the outcrop that displayed a surface of what geologists call desiccation mud cracks. The polygonal patterns that I was looking at recorded an ancient dry season with a drought that had once baked the delta. As the rains halted and the sun cooked the land, its soils shrank and cracked; the results were the polygons that I was looking at. They took me back through time; I felt the dry heat of the Devonian sun on my back.

Now I began to truly comprehend what I was looking at. Those seventy feet of sedimentary rock recorded an enormous length of time. That time, in turn, recorded a long chapter in the history of what has been called the "Catskill Delta." Long ago, during the Devonian, this delta had rivaled the Mississippi Delta in size. Many rivers descended mountain slopes to the east and all of them had flowed out across the delta to the Catskill Sea. They carried enormous amounts of sediment and left much of it here in what today we call the Catskill Mountains.

But there was much more: I realized that while I had traveled through time, what I had not done was to change my elevation. Sure I had first visited Old Orleans at an elevation of 1560 feet and now I was at 1740 feet, but these were just modern elevations. The downhill deposits of Old Orleans and the ones now before me were all formed at approximately sea level. Yes, 180 feet of sands and mud had been laid down, but at the same time the crust here had sunk those same 180 feet. I turned and looked downhill. In my mind's eye Old Orleans was now buried under 180 feet of sediment.

I walked up the road and reached the thirty feet of sedimentary rock that made up the top this outcropping. I soon found signs that these sandstones had once been another Devonian-age river. I saw what geologists call trough cross bedding and sheet laminations. These formed in the currents of the ancient river.

Now I had learned a great deal more. The crust of this, the Catskill Delta, had been slowly sinking. As sediments were brought to it and deposited, their weight had pressed down on the crust, and this is what had depressed it. A hundred feet of sediment would eventually accompany a hundred feet of subsidence. A thousand feet of sediment would witness a thousand feet of depression. The Catskill strata are many thousands of feet thick.

I stepped back and looked at the hundred-foot-thick outcropping. It represented a large slice of time. The Catskill Delta was accumulating vast quantities of sediment, and it was, at the same time, sinking. As the crust subsided, rivers would wander across the surface of the delta. There are lots of rivers on deltas;

that's what they are good at. I had already seen the "Little Mississippi" and now I was looking at the deposits of another river. I watched as, periodically, the delta flooded and, periodically, developed soils. I gazed as rivers meandered across its surface and then, again, I watched as droughts had baked the same lands. The outcrop was a history book.

I continued up the highway; what would I see next? The answer would be "more of the same." I passed the famous Point Lookout Restaurant and a little farther down the road there were more river sandstones. It was a repeat of the Cornwallville Exposure. There, before me, was the cross section of another river. It had the same sort of steep bank. But now, I had reached a modern elevation of 1,970 feet; my journey had carried me past about 400 feet of stratified rock. All of it consisted of petrified rivers and lithified delta plains. All of it was part of the Catskill Delta. Once, almost 400 million years ago, all this looked like today's Mississippi Delta. And 400 million years from now, it is quite likely that the Mississippi Delta will look like this.

But, then I thought about "Old Orleans." In my mind's eye, I stood on the Catskill delta plain and now Old Orleans lay buried beneath my feet, under 400 feet of sediment. How many years had that burial taken?—Tens of thousands?—Hundreds of thousands?—Millions? I did not know. But that Old Orleans had become deeply buried; it was now a fossil. It was a petrifaction buried deeply and only remembered by geologists. I gazed down the highway. In the far distance was the Old Orleans outcrop. I pondered how deeply it had come to be buried.

And with this thought, I found the wisdom I had been searching for. My journey had not been about Old Orleans, but instead, it had become a timely journey to New Orleans. That modern city has had its first taste of a geological inevitable. Geology will, given time, overcome this city. Like Old Orleans, the centuries and millennia will pass all too quickly. And they will carry New Orleans downward into first a shallow grave and then a very deep burial. New Orleans will someday be a fossil city, buried beneath hundreds and then thousands of feet of sedimentary rock. Its bricks and mortar and its asphalt and wrought iron will become components of a single thick stratum of rock. Its above-ground crypts will find themselves well below the surface, down where burial grounds should be. Man will struggle against all this. From time to time he will win a small skirmish, but it the end, he will lose. New Orleans, like Old Orleans, is a city condemned to enter the realm of paleontology.

This journey along Route 23 takes us first into the deep past, then to today's headlines and then on to the distant future. There is great wisdom to be found here. It is written in stone.

Kaatskill Life, Summer, 2006

SURFING CHANNELS

ONE OF THE MORE CONTROVERSIAL ISSUES facing environmental geologists in the Catskill Mountains is channelization. The word refers to a wide variety of engineering practices which alter the paths of river channels. Rivers can be straightened or relocated, their banks can be landscaped, their channels can be cleared, and so on. The goals can be aesthetic but most often the intent is to clear the channels in order to stabilize them and prevent floods.

Those are worthy goals and, if you have a home near a flood-prone river, channelization can be very attractive concept. But the strategy has its critics. Channelized streams are not natural streams; their habitats have been drastically altered along with their faunas and floras. Ironically channelization can promote flooding. That threat may be closer than you think.

Go to Dixon Avenue in Bearsville and drive to the bridge that crosses the Saw Kill. You can see a good example of a channelized stream here. For about a quarter mile downstream the channel has been cleared; it is broad and flat. The banks are steep and tall, having been sculpted by engineers, not Nature. For a short distance upstream, it is the same. I suspect that this stretch of the stream was stabilized to protect the bridge abutments.

If you want to see what the natural stream looked like here, travel upstream. Beyond the channelized stretch you will find the Saw Kill much as it was in its natural state. Look for criss-crossing channels, "dunes" of cobbles, and small islands with growths of young trees. Watch especially for broken dead trees, victims of long ago floods. The river is a mess, but that's as Nature made it. There's nothing very efficient about the Saw Kill as it was. Those cobble banks and broken trees are there because Nature couldn't get them down the river. There were too many impediments.

Not so in the channelized stretch which is almost clean as a whistle. Things don't get hung up there. During high flow the currents move things along and the channels remains flushed clean of debris. That's the problem.

If you hike downstream to the end of the channelized stretch, you will find that the river had always made a sharp turn to the left. Here's where things have gone wrong. During high flow tree trunks are efficiently carried to that bend in the river, then they slam into the bank and become hung up. Cobbles do the same thing and there are cobble banks abutting the tree trunks. This has blocked the

Opposite: **A debris jam on the Saw Kill. (Titus)**

river even more, and now, especially during floods, there is a sharp leftward lurch in the river current here. This has carried more tree trunks and more cobbles around the bend and piled them up. In effect, the channelized stretch of the Saw Kill is kept clean, but the debris that should be back there is piling up at that bend in the river. Nature is producing her own dam!

This may be reaching a critical point. The river here has become completely clogged with broken trees; a logjam dam seems to be near completion. Hence, in an effort to improve the flow of the river, channelization has instead created a dam. That, of course, makes a flood threat.

Now, I am not a thousand-dollar-a-day environmental consultant and my opinion doesn't count for much, but I think that this is the sort of thing people need to be aware of. There are no houses in the immediate vicinity, and so there probably is not immediate impending disaster, but I think that this should be looked into.

Woodstock Times, Oct. 1997

DRY BROOK IN FLOOD

W E USUALLY THINK OF FLOODS as springtime events, but sometimes they occur in the depths of winter. Winter floods are caused by a combination of unlucky events: first the accumulation of a heavy snow pack, then a warm spell with plenty of melting, and finally a hard warm rainfall. All three of these happened in the Catskills during the January of 1996. The resulting floods were terrible events, causing eight deaths with widespread and severe damage. These losses are always accompanied by psychological damage. People fear that the floods will return, and there is a great deal of anxiety that lasts for months. There is good cause for those fears, as floods do return.

Floods are, of course, of great interest to geologists, and the minimization of flood damage is a critical goal of modern environmental geology. There are many things that a community can do to reduce the potential threat of a flood, and geologists play an important role in this. Floods are of interest to traditional geologists as well. A great flood has a substantial effect upon geomorphology; it is one of the prime agents of landscape development. There is a close relationship between the shape of the valley and the many floods which have passed through it.

Opposite: **A flood deposit on Dry Brook. (Titus)**

Strangely, it is long after the waters have subsided that you can best go and see the effects of a flood. I had been meaning to explore Dry Brook for some time, but after the 1996 floods, I had a lot of extra motivation. I waited for high summer when the stream flow was low. You see, I didn't want to actually see the January flood itself; I wanted to see the aftereffects. A flood leaves a chaos of fresh sediment and broken trees, and what I wanted to see were those scars. Summer with its empty stream channels was the time for that. It's safer too, a lot safer!

Dry Brook is a tributary of the East Branch of the Delaware which is commonly called the Pepacton. Even though it is an out-of-the-way tributary, Dry Brook is not a small stream; it is more than ten miles long. But, as it is off the beaten path,

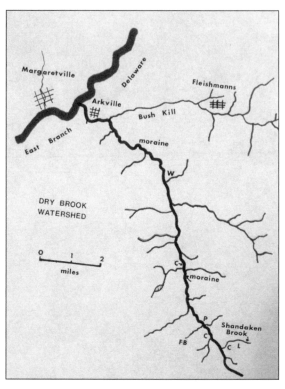

A map of Dry Brook. (Titus)

it's not terribly well known. Perhaps its most famous moment was when John Burroughs chose the creek to launch his small, homemade boat for his voyage down the Pepacton in the early 1880s.

The best way to explore a river is to hike to its upper reaches and then slowly work your way downstream. You begin where the river begins, and as you follow it, you watch as it grows larger and wider. With a trained eye or a good guide you can follow the development of a stream and really come to understand it. As Dry Brook is accessible from one end to the other, it's well-suited for the endeavor.

On my way there I passed through nearby Margaretville, which was among those towns that suffered greatly from the January flood. Before I visited the origin of that flood I wanted to see some of its damage. A lot of federal money had been made available and the town had been cleaned up quite a bit, but they were still rebuilding along the banks of the stream.

I continued on to Arkville and turned up Dry Brook Road until I reached the parking area for the yellow access trail. The trail took me up to the highest realms of the watershed. Here there is one of a small host of tributaries which constitute the "nursery" of the whole stream system. The yellow trail follows Dry Brook and then turns east into the clove of Shandaken Brook, which is the highest tributary of the watershed. The source of Shandaken Creek is found just upstream from the Shandaken lean-to.

In its upper reaches, Shandaken Brook is not all that impressive a stream, just a low stony creek bed surrounded by relatively gentle slopes. The valley here is a broad bowl, and I suspect that it was carved by a small Alpine glacier about 16,000 years ago. There isn't very much water at the head of a stream even at peak precipitation, so there are never any floods here. Without powerful flows of water there has not been much erosion, and thus there is not much landscape to see. The bowl is, however, ideal for catching rainwater and so it is here that the watershed begins.

It was July when I visited the brook, but in my mind it was January. I could easily imagine the large amounts of rapidly melting snow that had been here on that rainy January day. I saw thick, wet, gray mounds of it overhanging the banks of the stream. All along the stream's edge water was emerging from beneath the snow. It was warm, and dark pools of water formed in each of my boot prints. I kicked some snow into the stream; it instantly turned translucent, but did not melt. It was carried away quickly by the current—and then it was July again.

Just a short distance down the stream, the valley narrows and the Shandaken has carved a vee-shaped notch. This is really typical mountain landscape and, as you continue downstream, it gets better. Just south of the trail is a real treat—one of the prettiest little canyons I know of in the area. This canyon of rock is fundamentally different from that above. Here, the smooth vertical walls speak of numerous periods of high stream flow, times when Shandaken Brook had swollen into powerful flows. For millennia, surging waters have been funneled into this canyon and this has slowly steepened it. I pondered the recent winter here, and in my mind's eye, I could see the canyon nearly filled with rushing water. This must have been a lively place in January 1996, but a risky place to visit. Still, this wasn't *the* flood; the canyon here is very well-equipped to handle even this high flow.

Below the canyon much of the stream bed continues to be composed of sandstone. All of this bedrock is typical of the upstream end of a watershed. At the confluence with Flatiron Brook there is a small but very attractive waterfalls. Here the stream has carved another canyon through the falls. Flatiron Brook marks a profound change in the nature of the stream system. There are two parts to a watershed of this sort. The rocky upstream realm is largely responsible for eroding landscape; here rock is turned into sediment. Then there is a sediment-laden downstream stretch which is responsible for transporting all of those eroded materials. The falls at Flatiron Brook mark the boundary between the two realms.

It was in the next stretch of the valley that I finally found the real scars of the

A waterfall at confluence with Flatiron Brook. (Titus)

January flood. Below the falls, I found many temporary channels that had only been active during the peak of the flood. Back then, the rising waters had overflowed the main stream and split into multiple channels which criss-crossed across the valley flats. It would have been difficult and dangerous to visit this site during the flood, but my mind's eye brought me safely back to that January. I saw a riot of powerful, whitewater currents. They flowed past broken trees and bent brush. These noisy, choppy temporary channels continued all the way downstream to the trail head and parking area. But now it was July and these channels were dry, but they were still lined with the cobbles they carried during the flood.

Dry Brook valley has quite a geological past. It was extensively glaciated about 16,000 years ago. Alpine glaciers had formed in the upper reaches of the watershed and streams of ice descended down the valley. Glaciers are very good at transporting heavy sediment and that accounts for most of the boulders and cobbles that you see in the bed of the stream. You can find one of these heavily glaciated stretches of the river just above Haynes Hollow. Here the valley is crowded and clogged with debris called a glacial moraine. This deposit has diverted Dry Brook westward into another pretty bedrock canyon.

From here on downstream, exposed bedrock is seen only occasionally. Here the valley of Dry Brook is composed of sediment, and most of it is pretty coarse-grained stuff: gravel, cobbles and even boulders. This course sediment has a story

A cobble "dune" on Dry Brook. (Titus)

to tell. To have been brought here, there must have been strong flood currents, and that's what happened. If you know what to look for, you soon begin to see the evidence. As you descend the creek, you will commonly find large heaps of cobbles which have been sculpted into streamlined sinuous heaps. In effect these are "dunes" of cobbles, much like sand dunes but composed of much larger grains. These dunes record the moments of peak flooding. Sand dunes are sculpted by wind, that's all that is needed to move sand around, but cobble dunes were sculpted by raging flood torrents. When you see how large the cobbles are, and notice how high the dunes are, you quickly get a real sense of the magnitude of the flood. But in January, you couldn't have seen any of this because the dirty water was brown with sediment and white with foam; it hid what was going on beneath the surface. That's still another reason why July is the best month to see a January flood.

As I continued on to the middle stretch of Dry Brook, I saw that the stream had cut a broad swath during the January floods. With my January eyes, I could see how the then-powerful stream swept back and forth across the flood plain and left a large deposit of gravel and cobbles. There are houses, and it must have been here that January's Dry Brook had become dangerous.

I was well downstream now and I found more stories in the rocks. There were long, broad stretches of cobble-laden stream beds along the river. If you look carefully, you will find that nearly all of the cobbles are inclined in an upstream direction. This is normal; these cobbles have been oriented by the intense flood currents and that's called imbricate bedding. To a geologist, this is still another sign of the power of the recent flood.

Toward Arkville, Dry Brook passes through one more glacial moraine. Here again its many floods have carved another canyon through the glacial debris. It's a deep and narrow canyon and an impressive feature. When a powerful flood is funneled into such a tight squeeze, the confined currents are likely to become quite agitated. During the January floods, this must have been a frightening place - a swirling swollen, churning, loud cataract. When it emerged, the lower end of the canyon must have been like the nozzle of a fire hose—aimed downstream. It's only a mile to Arkville and then just another mile to Margaretville. Things were about to get very bad. Those two short miles would witness the full force of the flood.

For me it was January again. From east of Fleischmanns and north of Roxbury other streams were repeating the story of Dry Brook. Rivers were rising and channels were flooding. Just above Arkville, Dry Brook reaches a confluence with Bush Kill. That creek had also been rising actively, and it too was a scary sight. With the two streams joined, a terrible flow swept onward. The current would just miss the Arkville business district, as most of it is built about twenty feet

Imbricate bedding of boulders, they dip to the left, the water flowed to the right.
(Titus)

above the flood plain. But just below it and to the west the devastation began. Quite a few residences were destroyed and there was more damage to the river-banks. Then it got worse, just short of Margaretville there is the confluence with the East Branch of the Delaware River. With that, the combined strengths of these several flooding streams bore down the valley. Margaretville would have no good fortune on that day. Much of the town is just barely above the level of the river. Two local brooks, Binnekill and Bull Run, flow into town from the north and east. Both of these were also in full flood. The combined waters of all of these streams brought the terrible devastation we saw.

You can still sense some of the power of this event. Return to Dry Book Road at Arkville and view the stream bed of the combined Dry Brook/Bush Kill. In July the river flows back and forth through lazy meander loops, which is not surprising because downstream rivers do this. The meander belt shows just how wide the river was at the time of the flood. But what is most surprising is how much sediment there is. Much of the sediment is made up of cobbles, a very coarse deposit and that's unusual this far downstream. That's still another testimony to the power of the flood currents that carried these cobbles so far out of the mountains.

When I looked again, it was January again. I could see the powerful white-water torrents that disgorged from above and rushed by below. It was a rush of

Meandering channels cross gravels near Arkville. (Titus)

choppy, frothing foam with a roar that projected the full strength of its power. A geologist can see deeper though: I could peel away the water and see beneath the churning surface. Below there were other currents, flows of gravel, sand, and silt. The grains of sediment swirled by in agitated eddies. The gravel bounced up and down erratically. All of this material moved quickly down the stream like a driving blizzard of sediment. Beneath was still another slower current, a loudly clattering flow of agitated cobbles. They banged into each other, bounced up and down, and rolled over and over. This was something few people get to hear. It was a chaos of sediment all headed downstream. I was hearing a powerful current of sediment streaming out of the mountains!

And then it was July again. The water was almost gone, but the currents of cobbles lie where they were at the end of the flood. I watched bulldozers repairing the damage. More engineering was underway toward Fleischmanns. All this will probably help to delay the next flood—maybe. But for time immemorial people have tried to control rivers. It's a futile effort; when man fights Nature, Nature eventually wins.

Kaatskill Life, Spring 1997

TROUBLE IN THE LAND OF GILBOA

I WOULD LIKE TO TAKE YOU ACROSS TO MY SIDE OF THE RIVER. We have the makings of a classic environmental geology hazard developing here and it is certainly of regional interest.

It all started back in the 1920s when the Catskills village of Gilboa was sacrificed as New York City built a dam for its Schoharie Reservoir. People were moved out, and the town was razed to make way for the reservoir. There are still a lot of hard feelings about that. Many people of Schoharie Valley feel as if they were the native inhabitants in a colony of one of the old European imperial powers. In the last year or so those resentments have metamorphosed into fears, as we have seen potentially serious problems with the old dam.

Early this decade, an engineering firm conducted a survey of the dam's safety that uncovered structural problems. The dam is nearly eighty years old, and it has suffered a great deal of aging. Much of the stepped downstream stone facing had simply weathered away. It no longer broke up the current of water flowing over the crest of the dam, and the plummeting water had been cutting deep holes into the bottom of the downstream channel. The holes evidently threatened the stability of the whole dam, and they were fixed very, very quickly. But there was more.

The bedrock beneath the dam was found to be in uncertain condition. It was cut by horizontal fractures and horizontal seams of weathered rock. That meant that if enough water ever pushed against the dam, there might not be enough friction to prevent a catastrophe.

The worst-case scenario would involve the dam sliding forward just a bit and then breaking up. Quickly, a wall of water, forty feet or so deep, would start a rush down the Schoharie Creek Valley. Soon that torrent would reach the Blenheim Reservoir and the dam there would also quite likely be broken. Now, a combined flow of 25 million gallons of water would continue its turbulent journey north. In another hour or two the towns of Middleburgh and Schoharie would be overwhelmed by the tsunami. Nothing would stop the flow. It would continue north until reaching the Mohawk Valley, and there it would turn east. Quite a bit of its momentum would remain as it reached Schenectady.

There are thought to be about 8,000 people living in the path of this flood. It's just a question of how many of them would die. As I said, this is only a worst-case scenario; it's not likely to happen, but it does catch your attention, doesn't it? It won't surprise you to hear that a lot of people over on this side of the Hudson are quite alarmed by the prospects of such a disaster.

What exactly would trigger this awful event? The best estimate is that if floodwater ever reached a level eight feet above the top of the dam, then the dam would fail. In the past the worst floods have reached six feet above the top. Dam officials insist that the chances are very slim that the old record will ever be broken, but try to tell that to people who live downstream. They have banded together into a group that calls itself "Dam Concerned Citizens" They have been trying to make sure that, when repairs are made to the dam, they will be more than adequate. You can certainly understand their point of view.

Things have been happening. If you visit the reservoir today you will find that it is nearly empty. Virtually all of its water has been drained south down the Shandaken Tunnel and into the Ashokan Reservoir. Right now there is no pressure on the dam and little to fear in the immediate future. The plans are to literally bolt the old dam down. Holes will be drilled into underlining bedrock and giant clamps will hold the dam in place. Of course, that assumes the bedrock is strong enough. We will see.

EDITORIAL NOTE: A great deal of progress was made and by 2007 things looked quite a bit better at Gilboa.

The Independent, May, 2005

THE PRESIDENT IN A SLUMP

THE EAST BANK OF THE HUDSON RIVER was once a very fashionable location where only the *very best* people lived. Such times and attitudes have faded, but a legacy still remains; along that bank of the river a large number of very fine old mansions can be seen. Vanderbilts, Livingstons, Roosevelts and other notables may or may not live there anymore but many of their old homes remain as public parks. Well cared for, these should all last a very long time. But just how long is "a very long time?"

To a geologist the answer is, "well, not so long." When I visited the Vanderbilt and Roosevelt mansions recently, I noticed that the two had something in common. Both are built upon the same geological foundations and both, eventually, may face the same fates.

Wander around the grounds of the Vanderbilt Estate. You will very likely enjoy seeing an abundance of very old and very large ornamental trees. And then there is the house itself, it's quite a sight too. What you probably won't notice, at least not right away, is how flat the grounds are. This is no accident; we are looking at the top of a delta on the shores of Glacial Lake Albany, the great ice age lake that once filled the Hudson Valley. Delta tops are flat as a pancake. The fine grained mud that accumulates upon them settles down in flat sheets. But Glacial Lake Albany is long gone; it drained about 14,000 years ago. Since then the effects of gravity have worked on the old lake's delta and sharpened already steep slopes overlooking the river. That's what made the Vanderbilt site such a desirable location. The house sits upon a high flat plateau, commanding a very fine view of the Hudson. The Vanderbilt's couldn't resist it.

All this is also the case for the Roosevelt home and, in fact, for all of the town of Hyde Park itself. But, scenic though this might be, there are long term hazards. Those steep slopes are not accidental; there is a pattern here and Nature is sending out a warning. These slopes are the headwalls of what geologists call "slumps." What has happened here is that large cohesive masses of old lake muck have detached along curved fractures and slid downwards. This is an intermittent phenomenon, it happens occasionally during relatively brief periods of movement and then there is little activity for very long periods of time. The hazard is thus somewhat like that of an earthquake: long periods of quiet interrupted by moments of destructive activity.

What triggers a slump? Most likely they result from periods of very wet weather. The old lake sediments become waterlogged and unstable. They become

Steep slope behind the Roosevelt mansion. (Titus)

very soft and go through an episode of slumping. By the time that is over, the climate has probably dried out enough to delay further action for another long while.

Wander the grounds of these fine old mansions and you will soon find a number of large semicircular slump features, places where, long ago, slumps occurred. At the bases of those large semicircles the ground is hummocky. Those are the scars of the old slides. The landscape speaks to us of slumps long past, but it also speaks to us of events yet to come. Someday, I hope not until a very long time from now, the land beneath one of these fine old mansions will likely become wet and unstable. The earth will heave and the mansion will collapse. It's a sad fate for some fine old homes, but Nature does not discriminate in favor of the wealthy; Nature does not care.

Woodstock Times, 1999

WHAT'S HAPPENING TO US?

WHEN THINGS start to go downhill the trend often starts out so slowly that nobody is aware that there is a problem. Once downhill motions have accelerated it is often too late to do anything about them. I have been increasingly concerned that I have been watching some troubling geological developments. Over the past five years I have been noticing an increase in the frequency of landslides in the Catskills and Hudson Valley region. There was a bad one in Delmar several years ago. A year or so later we saw a similar event in Schenectady. Not only was there a slide there but six houses had to be abandoned. More slides soon occurred in Rensselaer, Livingston and Greenport.

Then there were flooding problems. In a number of locations in Columbia County people began complaining that their basements, which often had always been dry, were beginning to flood with some frequency. As a geologist with something of a public profile, people brought my attention to their problems and so it was that I began to suspect that something was going on. Two years ago we had a landslide just down the road from our house in Freehold. I guess that was "enough is enough." I began to cover the story.

But this was the "things start to go downhill slowly" part of the situation. Nothing too alarming was going on, except to alarmists like me. It was last year that things began to go downhill rapidly. You may remember the awful rains of late June 2006. It got to be so bad that roads were closed all through the Catskills, especially in Delaware County. What happened is that flooding, and all of the secondary events associated with flooding, came to be added to my watch list.

We had several inches of rain over a short period of time. Creeks and rivers all over the Catskills rose up and expanded beyond their banks. Flooding began quickly, and it got to be pretty bad. There was flooding in the major towns all along the Susquehanna River. There were also a large number of floods in Delaware County, and we saw the same along Catskill Creek.

The effects of flooding are well known; it is something we see in the television news all the time. Basements fill up with water and so too, sometimes, half of the first floors of houses. People usually escape with their lives but the damage to their homes can be frightful.

But there are a lot of other things. Flood waters tend to slow down where they encounter bridge abutments. The powerful currents undermine the abutments and bridges can collapse. This happened last June and it happened to a lot of places.

Flooding on Catskill Creek. *Below:* **Dark line marks flooding in a basement. (Titus)**

Houses positioned too close to the stream banks can be damaged or even swept away. It is not unusual to see half of a house hanging above the stream at the end of the flood. I saw a number of photographs of just this sort.

Then there is the phenomenon that first caught my attention: the earth slide. This often comes late in the sequence. The ground fills up with gluts of ground-

Flood-collapsed bridge. (Titus) *Below:* **Highway damage on
Route 23A in Kaaterskill Clove. (Courtesy of NYSDOT)**

water. That lubricates the soils and adds a great deal of hydrostatic pressure. Eventually the earth just gives way and a large, cohesive mass of earth slides downhill, leaving a big curved scar behind. It looks at lot like a giant with a giant ice cream scoop had gone to work on the slope. That's apparently what happened in Kaaterskill Clove. A short stretch of the clove highway (Route 23A) was taken out when the earth beneath it simply slid downhill. I never saw this, authorities would not let anyone in, but photographs suggest that this is exactly what happened.

This slide was one of the worst aspects of the June flooding. Route 23A had been closed for much of the spring for routine roadwork, but now it would be out for many months, and that meant something of an economic catastrophe for the villages of Tannersville and Hunter. The summer tourist trade was badly affected. If repairs were delayed, the winter ski season would be threatened. That's serious business here in the Catskills, but luckily repairs were finished just in time.

What caused the slide? It's easy to blame such adverse climatic events on bad luck, but I have been following this story for years, and I am afraid that there is something worse afoot than plain bad luck. The commonality that runs through all of this is climate change. We have all become aware of global warming, and increasingly, many of us have begun to fear its adverse effects. Has global warming come to the Catskills and is the increased rainfall and increased flooding all part of the global trend? Maybe.

The scientist who wants to answer such question needs a good deal of information (we call it "data"). Fortunately, they have been collecting climatic data in Albany for a long time. When I looked up the weather records I found that there has been nearly no change in temperature over the past century. It has grown warmer, but only by a scant one tenth of a degree. This is certainly not enough to have disrupted the climate and produced the awful results.

But I kept looking, and I did find something else. The climate has, indeed, changed; it's grown wetter. Back during the 1960s there was an awful multi-year drought. I remember that; I saw some of my favorite ponds (kids love ponds) completely dry up during those years. But, since that time, there has been a very substantial increase in rainfall. In fact, the rainfall has risen by 16%. That's a lot.

That means that all of our rivers and creeks carry a lot more water than they used to. It also means that our grounds must be more water-soaked than they were in the past. So, it can hardly be a surprise that when seasonal rainfall rises above the already high averages, then things will happen. We got a very good (really very bad) taste of that in June 2006.

Is this related to global warming? I don't know. Here I am going to do a little scientific speculation. I will "hypothesize" not "theorize," there is a big difference. There is something called the North Atlantic Oscillation. It turns out that there are times when great high pressure systems park themselves over the Canary Islands in the eastern Atlantic. At the same time an unusual low pressure system prevails over Iceland. The result of all this is that during the winter an unusually large number of warm rainy storms (nor'easters) pass northward along the East Coast. Our late winters and early springs become very rainy and so too is our whole annual climate. It turns out that our North Atlantic Oscillation was very poorly developed during the 1960s when we saw droughts. But, and this is important, the Oscillation had been well developed ever since. The suggestion here is that it is the Oscillation that has caused our problems. But, I remind you, that is just hypothesis.

All this begs a big question: what is *going* to happen? I, of course, don't know, but I think I see some evidence that the North Atlantic Oscillation is weakening. If so, we may have seen the worst of what has been happening. But if I am wrong we may be in for a lot more of what we have been seeing.

So, I am concerned, and I guess there are good reasons for that. What might happen? The answer to that is more of the same, but maybe worse. I fear that the flooding we have seen in 2006 may continue. Houses and highways, built too close to rivers, will suffer as never before. Kaaterskill and Plattekill Cloves are likely to experience more washouts and this may have economic consequences.

Then there are the landslides. These slow, downhill motions of waterlogged earth can be quite hazardous. I would expect to see more in Kaaterskill Clove, but there are other locations at risk. The most slide prone geological features are old ice age deltas. We see a lot of them in the Hudson Valley where Glacial Lake Albany accumulated many delta deposits. They are much less common in the Catskills, but there is one place really at risk. I have long feared that we might see one of these slumps in the city of Oneonta. The town is built on an old delta and it might give way during some rainy season. Watch especially Cliff Street in Oneonta.

There are more frightening danger zones across the Hudson from us. The town of Hyde Park has two national landmarks: The Roosevelt family home, "Springwood," and the Vanderbilt mansion. Both are built on the very edge of a very big ice age delta. Either or both might give way and slide toward the Hudson some day. Wouldn't that cause a storm?

I hope that I am wrong, but this may all be serious business. We will all have to watch the weather forecasts more carefully in the future. It may not be as much weather as it is climate.

Kaatskill Life, Winter 2006-2007

PART FIVE

The Ice Age

RIVER OF ICE AT SUNSET

AUTUMN IS A GIFT, especially in the Catskills. This season of leaves is the time of the year to get out and enjoy a farewell to the warm weather. The heart of this scenic season extends from the middle of September to the middle of October. These are times when the first winter high-pressure systems come billowing out of Canada. They bring clear, dry, but still warm air masses to the Catskills. With them comes a clarity of the atmosphere and a scenery unmatched the rest of the year. There are a great number of wonderful fall landscapes well worth a visit. It is a terrible shame to let this time pass by without getting out. Take advantage of the autumn; winter is so long!

There are some scenic views which stand out, literally above others. Some of the truly great Catskill views can be found at North/South Lake State Park. From the edge of the escarpment on the Catskill Front there is a seventy-mile panorama of the Hudson Valley. Turn around and there is a view of the neighboring Catskill peaks. People have been drawn to North Lake since the early nineteenth century when the first road was cut up the mountain. During the late nineteenth and early twentieth centuries this was the site of the famed Catskill Mountain House Hotel, once the premier resort hotel of America. Today the location is part of the Catskill Forest Preserve.

After entering the park, drive to North Lake itself and hike north on the blue trail. It's an easy walk for most people, young and old. You are following in the paths of thousands of hikers who have visited here over the past two centuries. Almost all these people have been greatly affected by the scenery here.

The trail takes you along the very edge of the Catskill Escarpment. At some places it passes within a few feet of a shear cliff. Along the way you will pass Artist's Rock and eventually you will reach the yellow trail turnoff. Follow this to its end and there you will reach a ledge named "Sunset Rock" after a great boulder there. Before you is one of the grandest views in all of the Catskill Mountains.

The view from Sunset Rock. (Titus)

To the east is that seventy-mile view of the Hudson Valley with the Taconic Mountains beyond. To the south is the view of North and South Lakes and to their east is South Mountain. Beyond them you can just make out the upper reaches of Kaaterskill Clove and still farther away are Roundtop Mountain and High Peak.

It's an impressive sight to say the least, and it's one which has played a role in the development of American art. Virtually all of the great nineteenth-century landscape artists, beginning with Thomas Cole, came here. They set up their easels or sketched here and turned out canvases portraying the site at different times of the year and different times of the day. Watch for work by Cole, Sanford Robinson Gifford, Jasper Cropsey, William Henry Bartlett and others.

But I am a geologist and, while I greatly admire those artists and their work, I see other things from this site. I sit on Sunset Rock and look north, and soon I can see it as it was 23,000 years ago. As I watch, the years and decades pass by rapidly. The climate slowly turns cold and soon it is becoming Arctic. As the decades and centuries elapse, the forests turn sickly gray and then die. The skies are usually blue and sunny, but cold dry gale winds blow out of the northeast. They shatter the brittle old tree limbs.

To the north a low whiteness appears in the Hudson Valley. It is dark blue in the morning, radiantly white at noon and aquamarine just before dark. As time continues its passage, this white advances south and its image focuses into that of an advancing glacier. It passes beneath the Sunset Rock ledge and continues down the Hudson. Slowly the swell of ice thickens. Like a stream in flood, the ice slowly rises and fills the valley. It laps up onto the Catskill Front and soon a stream of white overflows the valley and advances southwestward across what someday will be North and South Lakes. The moving ice is very erosive and it's beginning to scour out these basins.

Now even more ice pours down the Hudson. All along the Catskill Front, ice is overflowing the valley and still it continues to thicken. Next comes the great swell of the main glacier, an ice sheet at least 3,000 feet thick. The white soon overwhelms this entire region. It continues to advance southwestward until all of the Catskills are entombed. The whole region becomes a great white, high Arctic plain. That may be a somber vision to have on a beautiful autumn afternoon, but that is what I see from Sunset Rock.

Woodstock Times, Sept. 1996

AN UNPLANNED VIEW

I HAVE BEEN INVITED to do an event at Olana on the morning of August 11, 2003. Olana is the grand old Persian Revival mansion built by Frederic Church in the 1860s. Church was the most financially successful painter of the Hudson River School of Art. He began building his home soon after reaching the pinnacle of his success, but just before rheumatoid arthritis began crippling his talented hands. Church would eventually have to quit painting, but he went on to make Olana the art of the last third of his life. Today Olana towers above the eastern end of the Rip Van Winkle Bridge as a monument to the great painter.

Church employed a strategy that was popular with landscape architects of the Hudson Valley at that time. He incorporated "planned views" into his landscape designs. This reflected a growing appreciation for nature, a philosophy that has blossomed into the environmentalism of our time.

The grandest of his planned views is seen from the side porch of the house. Look one way and you see the expanse of the Hudson Valley; look another way and there before you are all the Catskills.

Nearly every part of his 200 acres was landscaped with views in mind. Every bend in the driveway, every trail and every knoll seems to present the visitor with another fine vista. Many of the best views have now been blocked by growing trees. But much remains as Church had intended. My event will be a walk around the grounds. We will take in some of scenery as Frederic Church designed it, but I mostly aim to look into the past in order to see the great unplanned views of Olana. Anyone can see the view from the porch as it is today. Here is what I see:

Olana, September 23rd, 135,892 years B.C. late afternoon—It is a typical September afternoon of the Illinoisan phase of the Ice Age. An enormous high-pressure system chills the land all the way to the pole and beyond to Scandinavia.

Relentless winds are driving out of the northeast. Earlier in the day, no views could be seen through the blowing snow. But now the winds are abating at last. A blue sky is beginning to break through, and as the winds quiet, more of the landscape appears. In the dry Arctic air, the view is perfectly clear; to the south-west are the peaks of the Catskills and snow banks abut the mountains like aprons of white. The winds generate wispy currents of snow that rise and fall like foamy waves breaking upon the rocky "shores" of the Catskill Front.

Despite the snow, quite a bit of bedrock can be seen. The mountains are bare with no hint of brown soil or green foliage. The brick red of lower horizons of rock grades upward into strata of light buff color. These are not the green Catskill Mountains we know today.

The aprons of snow grade downwards onto a great valley glacier. The entire Hudson Valley is filled with ice. The northern half of that glacier is white, deeply blanketed in last winter's accumulation of snow.

Farther south, where the recent summer has taken its toll, the fresh snow thins and old ice is exposed. Its rough, dirty surface displays crevasses, great fissures that are mostly curved to the south. They are lined up, closely spaced, and parallel to each other. The crevasses are dark blue black, while the ice in between them is brilliant white with a thin, recent snow cover.

The ice has fractured this way because the mid-valley portions of the glacier have been advancing more quickly than the adjacent ice that drags along the Catskill Front. That ice is slowed down. The crevasses thus betray the motions of the glacier, but all of it is much too slow to be perceived. To the south, the crevasses widen and deepen. Here a lot of melting has occurred during the brief "summer," and the crevasses are more shadowed and a darker shade of blue.

More to the west, where the glacier abuts the slopes of the Catskill Front, the grinding ice is steepening the wall of rock. This is an icy machine of erosion that is carving and sculpting the finishing touches of the great escarpment, called the Wall of Manitou. Southward from this, the ice flows are pigmented with wide stripes of reddish brown.

One familiar feature is missing. While there is a break between High Peak and South Mountain, there is no Kaaterskill Clove. The great chasm has not yet been cut into the Wall. It will have to wait until after the Illinoisan glaciers are gone from the valley.

As the sun sets above the Catskills, the shadows of the mountains lengthen across the ice. There is no moon, and the scene quickly darkens. Gradually the green and red drapery of northern lights appears. The aurora takes the form of a great arch, which soon stretches from above the southern Wall of Manitou to the far northern end of the Northeastern Escarpment. The lights shimmer very brightly in the darkening, still night.

The Independent, August 2003

THE GREAT LAKE OF THE CATSKILLS

SOMETIMES THINGS are so large that we cannot see them. That is the case in landscape geology as well as in other fields. The very largest geological feature of the Catskills that I know of may well be one of the very least known. The fact is that, although it is no longer here, it has left a great deal of evidence. This invisible and missing geological feature is Glacial Lake Grand Gorge, the largest lake there ever was within the Catskills. The lake filled in most of the valleys of the upper reaches of the Schoharie Creek drainage basin. It extended from North Blenheim, in the north, to Grand Gorge, in the west, and, from there, to Windham and Hunter in the east. Its waters ranged from very shallow to depths of at least hundreds of feet. It was big lake but, as I said, it is entirely gone.

The story of Glacial Lake Grand Gorge goes back to the early days of the study of Catskill glaciations. Geologists had known that a great continental glaciation had once overrun the Catskills. That glaciation had not stopped until it reached a line stretching from Cape Cod to Long Island and then on through northern New Jersey and westward through Pennsylvania. That glaciation has come to be called the Woodfordian advance.

But, by the middle 1930s, our regional glacial geologists were becoming aware that there had been some secondary glaciations which occurred after the main event. One of these was an advance of ice that included a great finger of ice which penetrated the Schoharie Creek Valley and advanced through the Middleburgh vicinity. This valley glacier continued southward, and branches of it extended into all of the major tributary valleys of the Schoharie Creek system.

At its peak, this glacial advance reached the far corners of the Schoharie Creek drainage system. However, it did not have the momentum to overtop the central escarpment of the Catskills, and so it never extended beyond that line. Eventually the weather warmed and the advance stalled. Soon the great valley glacier was retreating, and the ice began vacating the Schoharie Creek valleys.

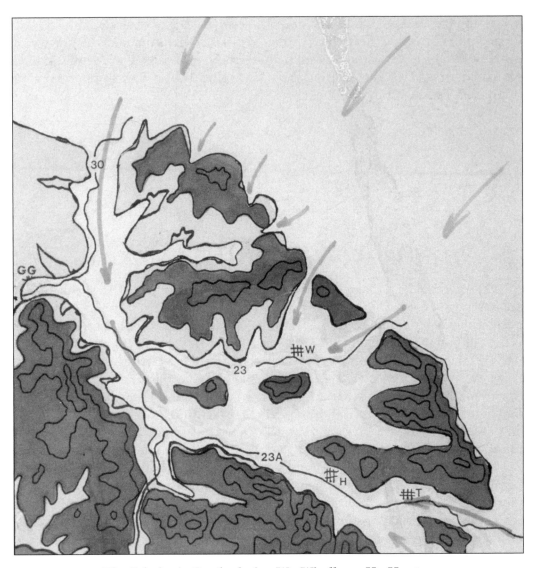

**The Schoharie Creek glacier. W - Windham, H - Hunter,
T - Tannersville, GG - Grand Gorge. (Titus)**

This left a problem behind. Where would all the water go? Today, Schoharie Creek waters flow north past Middleburgh and on to the Mohawk River and thence to the Hudson. But that was impossible back then, as a solid wall of ice blocked all flow to the north. Meltwater had nowhere to go, and it simply filled the empty valleys left behind. It filled those valleys, that is, until they overflowed.

It was only a matter of time until the meltwater would find some gap in the south and cascade through it; that gap would be the one at Grand Gorge. Some sort of opening had probably already been there. It was probably the product of

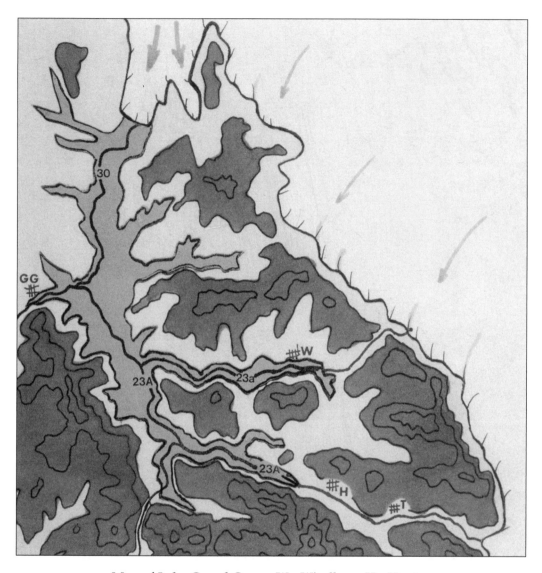

**Map of Lake Grand Gorge. W - Windham, H - Hunter,
T - Tannersville, GG - Grand Gorge. (Titus)**

rivers eroding up the opposite sides of the mountain. But when the meltwater began to pour through the gap, its geomorphology would have changed suddenly and very rapidly. The sloping upper reaches of the gap probably date back to that earlier era, but the walls of the lower third of the gap are nearly vertical. These are the walls of a ravine. They appear to have been cut by rushing waters acting like a chainsaw, cutting into the mountain. Through this gap the meltwater entered into the Delaware drainage system, passed between New Jersey and Pennsylvania and flowed into Delaware Bay.

And a lot of water passed this way. As the Schoharie Creek glacier melted back to the north, an increasingly large lake was left behind. From the lake all of the meltwater flowed south through the gap. More and more of our Catskill landscape became lake floor. The village of Grand Gorge was at the bottom of the lake. So too was the town of Prattsville. North of Prattsville, it was especially easy for the ice to block the Schoharie Creek Valley. The valley is narrow there and the walls are steep so the glacier plugged the valley with no chance of a leak. Here for quite some time the sites that would become Gilboa, North Blenheim, and Breakabeen lay submerged. All of these sites slumbered beneath the icy waters of Lake Grand Gorge, at its maximum.

But glacial lakes are temporary features; given time, the dams of ice will melt and the waters will find quicker and easier ways to drain into the sea. The history of Glacial Lake Grand Gorge came to an end when a new outlet opened up. When the retreating front of ice reached the Middleburgh vicinity, waters were able to reach the upper stretches of Catskill Creek and flow through Franklinton and on into the Hudson River. Much of the waters of Lake Grand Gorge exited the Schoharie Creek and only a very small lake was left behind. Eventually ice retreated entirely from Schoharie Creek, and no lakes were left.

That should have been the end of the story, but it was not. Many thousands of years later, when a growing New York City became thirsty for large water resources, man began to repeat what glaciers had once done. The city built dams, not of ice, but of cement, to block the northward flow of water to the Mohawk. The several reservoirs of the Schoharie Creek Valley are the result. These dams and their reservoirs are widely considered great works of engineering skill, but what man can do pales in significance compared to what Nature has done in these valleys.

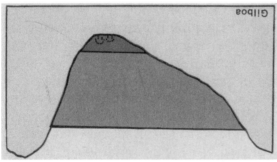

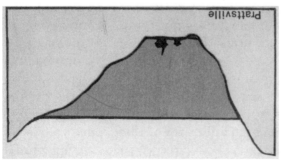

Top: Profile of the lake at Prattsville. Above: Profile of the lake towering above the reservoir at Gilboa. Opposite: Grand Gorge Gap. (Titus)

April 27th, the year 12,105 BC—We stand on what will someday be Route 30 with a view of Grand Gorge to the south. Barely visible, just to the east, lays a massive glacier. The front of the ice spreads around to the south in a large semicircle, which fills the entire valley. Below the ice, and extending off to the west, is a large cold, dark lake. What is most surprising about the scene is how comfortable the temperature is.

It has already been extremely warm for the past several years. The past winter had been very mild, and spring melting of the glacier is already well under way. But this year is really different. The El Niño effect has been most dramatic this year; the easterlies of the eastern Pacific Ocean have settled into complete doldrums, and without their cooling effect, the waters of the western Pacific have warmed and the sea has swollen. Heated water expands, and this year's sea levels are already fourteen inches above normal. Great masses of warm, moist air billowed out of the western Pacific, and, like hot air balloons, they have been sailing across the equator, and then deflecting northeastward into California. Rainfall there has been enormous, beyond anything seen here in millennia. The weather patterns continue east by northeast across North America. This is drawing warm, wet air up the Carolina coast. One after another intense, warm nor'easters have been striking the Catskills.

April 27th is the second day of the worst nor'easter of the season. When a warm, moist storm flows up and onto a glacier, the result is even more rainfall than would normally be the case. When a nor'easter collides with a glacier the results are far beyond what modern people are likely to be able to imagine. Two days of heavy, drenching, unrelenting rain have been pounding on the Catskills and their glaciers. The storm has stalled along the edge of the ice and another day of pounding rain lies ahead.

The glacier is a mess. It was not just melting in the presence of this deluge; it is disintegrating. It is breaking up into a crowded myriad of icy-blue jagged blocks. The driving rains drain into the crevasses between the blocks and fast currents of warm meltwater zigzag back and forth within the ice. From these currents, enormous and loud rushes of water are cascading out of the great crevasses that lay at the front of the glacier. Every few moments the quiet is shattered by the explosive sound of large, wet masses of slushy ice collapsing into the lake. A dense ice flow is drifting slowly toward the south. The ice is being drawn by a very strong current toward the distant gap.

From a perch above the northeast side of the Grand Gorge Gap the view is different. It is a strange phenomenon, but from here there are two entirely different sets of sights and sounds. To the east the distant break-up of the glacier can be seen but hardly heard. The flow of ice can be watched as it slowly approaches from across the lake. All is nearly silent in this direction.

Below, however, the currents speed up as they are sucked into the gap. As the

little bergs approach, they become crowded and interfere with the smooth flow of water. The currents break up into a whitewater froth. This is made worse by the narrowness of the gap. In effect, Grand Gorge Gap is a horizontal waterfall, its current not falling, but squeezing between to two towering walls of rock. It is this strange, powerful horizontal waterfall which has carved Grand Gorge Gap and named the town.

Kaatskill Life, Winter 1995-1996

THE CLAVERACK GIANT

COLUMBIA COUNTY is noted for many positive things. Some of them are recorded on those blue and gold historic marker signs you see along the highways. Such signs, however, don't often list major scientific breakthroughs. Nevertheless something very important scientific discoveries did occur here.

This county is the site of the fist discovery of that ice age emblem, the mastodont. This event dates back to the year 1705, when a Dutch colonialist came across a fossil tooth on the banks of the Hudson River at what was then the edge of the town of Claverack, just north of the city of Hudson. The name of our discoverer seems to have been lost to history. It's a shame as this was, without doubt, the most memorable thing he ever did.

The tooth certainly was remarkable. Most of the root had decayed away, but the enamel still gleamed. And it was big, weighing in at four and three-quarters pounds. Evidently, our colonial discoverer thought little enough of it, as he sold the tooth to Assemblyman Peter Van Bruggen for a gill of rum.

Van Bruggen brought the tooth to Albany, where Edward Hyde, Viscount of Cornbury and governor of the New York Colony, obtained it. Cornbury is most famous for supposedly dressing in women's clothing, but that is another story altogether. He showed a more scientific side of his nature with his interest in the tooth; he wondered what it represented.

Cornbury wouldn't keep the specimen to himself; he sent it off to England's foremost scientific organization, the Royal Society in London. In the letter he sent along with it, Cornbury reflected upon the various ideas that had been proposed to explain the fossil. There were two hypotheses; some people thought the tooth to have come from some remarkable beast or fish. Cornbury doubted that; he though the tooth was human, the remains of an ancient giant.

Based on the science of his time, his hypothesis was not as outlandish as it sounds today, I know what a mastodont is, and chances are you do too. Today we are comfortable with the idea of prehistoric creatures, as we have seen them in museums, on TV, and in the movies. But back then, nobody, absolutely nobody, had ever imagined such an animal as a mastodont. Not only had no one even ever heard of such a prehistoric monster, but nobody had heard of prehistory.

The notion of prehistory would have been quite an unwelcome revelation to Cornbury. He very likely thought, like almost all westerners, that the world was only about 6,000 years old, the direct creation, at that moment, of God.

So, if there was no prehistory and no prehistoric monsters, then exactly what did Cornbury believe the creature to be?

When he used to term "giant," he was referring to the Bible quote, "There were giants in the Earth those days."

To his credit, Cornbury sent men to search the Claverack site for more evidence, and they were successful. Sort of. Cornbury's crew did locate the skeleton and made efforts to dig it up, but the bones were so decayed that they mostly disintegrated as they came to the surface. The crew did estimate the skeleton was thirty feet long. And perhaps it had been much bigger than that; a limb bone was found, and before it had disintegrated, it was estimated to be seventeen feet long. A halo of discolored earth surrounded the skeleton, and that was seventy-five feet long.

Lord Cornbury's view that this was a biblical giant was enthusiastically embraced by the prominent Puritan minister Cotton Mather, of Witch Trial fame. Mather had once studied to be a physician and had a strong interest in natural history. He, like many ministers of his time, believed that an understanding of nature would confirm the Old Testament account of Earth history.

The sediments in which the Claverack giant had been found had been deposited, Mather thought, by the Great Deluge. Such views may seem quaint today, but in the eighteenth century this was legitimate science. The teeth and bones were, Mather argued, the remains of an Antediluvian giant and Mather wanted to prove that.

At that time, he was working on a book to be entitled *Biblia Americana,* and in it would be the latest scientific evidence for the Creation and the Flood. The Claverack giant was important science to Cotton Mather.

But there were other opinions. From the very beginning in 1705, there were people who had referred to the Claverack teeth as being like the ivory of an "Olivant," using an old spelling for elephant. The skeleton was not that of a human giant but one of Nature's giants, the elephant. This was still a very theological view, as the poor creature would have been regarded as having been also a victim of the Flood. And it must have been quite a flood to have swept a tropical animal so far from its natural setting.

The debate was a long one, and it was not finally settled until a good skeleton of an extinct mastodont turned up in the southern Hudson Valley in the early nineteenth century. Our mastodont turned out to be the first extinct species to be discovered anywhere and also pretty much the first prehistoric animal, as well.

It can be argued that two very substantial concepts of science got their starts in Columbia County. These are the notions of prehistory and extinction, and they are both terribly important in our modern views of Earth history. Curiously, few, if any, more fossil mastodonts have been found here. Most the best mastodont discoveries were made in Orange County. No matter, Columbia County still can, and should, claim these important distinctions.

The Independent, December 2002

BAD DAY ON DIAMOND STREET

SOME DAYS are worse than others. I would like to describe one of the worst ever for the city of Hudson. This was an environmental disaster about as bad as can be imagined. Like so many others that we worry about, this one involved global warming. But this was warming much more extensive than you and I will ever see, I hope. Let's get on with the story.

The last Ice Age began to come to an end about 18,000 years ago. A great continental ice sheet had advanced as far as Long Island, and as the climate warmed, it began to retreat. Researchers at Woods Hole Oceanographic Institute have found recently that by 13,400 years ago, the ice sheet had melted back to the northern tip of the Adirondacks. That set up a very perilous situation. Just to the west was an enormous ice age lake. Called Glacial Lake Iroquois, it was located where Lake Ontario is, but it was about three times bigger.

The waters of the lake were trapped behind dams composed of the Adirondacks to the east, and the ice sheet itself to the north. But that dam was about to break. This was a time of serious global warming. Glacial meltwater already flowed south through two large lakes. One, Glacial Lake Vermont, filled the Champlain Lowland. The other, Glacial Lake Albany, filled much of the Hudson Valley. Western Columbia County and all of the city of Hudson were already under the waters of Lake Albany, but it was going to get much worse.

Back north, the retreating ice was about to leave behind just a tiny, little hole in the dam. As the ice sheet melted away, it retreated from the northern tip of the Adirondacks, and water rushed through the opening. The small gap quickly became a very large one, and the icy tsunami cascaded down through Lake Vermont and on to Lake Albany.

To call this a catastrophic flood is an enormous understatement. This is what happened: In a very short period, Glacial Lake Iroquois dropped about 400 feet. Think about how much water that involved! All of that water was funneled into those two relatively narrow lowlands. That spelled major trouble.

That gets us back to Hudson. Over a period of what much have been just hours, the waters of Lake Albany must have swelled upward and turned into a roiling, churning, foaming chaos of broken ice and frigid ice water. The power and rage of that flow are difficult to imagine. None of us will ever see its like, I hope.

What I am portraying is a rising of the Lake Albany waters to levels far above what had been seen, but not for long. Down the Hudson Valley, near the Verrazano-Narrows Bridge of today, there was a great earthen dam. Our flood-waters soon backed up behind that dam and then began eroding into it. First a small notch was cut, and then waters poured through. Soon the flow cut a great gap in the dam.

With the dam broken, the water of Lake Albany rapidly poured out into the Atlantic. In Hudson that meant a sudden drop in water levels. Soon the lake waters shrank down to a narrow, but very erosive, flow. This quickly cut a deep Hudson River channel. When all this was done and things settled down, Hudson probably looked a lot more like its modern self. Something similar to today's river flowed by.

But, before then, that mighty erosive flow must have taken quite a toll upon our local geography. I wish I could point out some features that were shaped at that time but, for now, I can't. I can tell you that there are boulders the size of small cars that have been found offshore of New York City, and these are thought to have been carried out to sea by this tsunami. It takes a strong current to move something like that, and it almost frightens me to just imagine how strong. But, some days are worse than others.

The Independent, Feb. 2007

BIG ROCK FEST

JUNE IS THE TIME to visit North/South Lake State Park. If you have not been there, the park is one of the gems of the New York State park system. Of course, two gorgeous lakes are there. More than that, there are several miles of trails run-

Boulder Rock. Titus

ning along the great Catskill escarpment. Anywhere along the escarpment trail you can see a grand view of about seventy miles of the Hudson Valley. Beyond that, there are more trails into the woods and up into the mountains. If you don't like hiking, you can camp, swim, or picnic.

But my main attraction to North Lake has been the rocks, and there are some very good ones here. Let's go look at one of the best. Enter the park (they charge admission by the carload) and drive all the way to North Lake itself and park. Hike south toward the Catskill Mountain House site (follow signs for the hotel site and the blue trail). The hotel is long gone, but the site is still a clear field with a great cliff and magnificent view. You can see the Hudson River and the Taconic Mountains beyond. If you know where to look, you can see the village of Catskill, Frederick Church's mansion, Olana, and many other sites of the Hudson Valley.

The hotel was pretty expensive so enjoy the view; a century ago you probably couldn't afford it! Find the signs for the blue trail and follow them up the hill. You will ascend a couple of hundred feet in elevation, and quite steeply at first. Eventually the trail will level out upon one of those great ledges that are so typical of the Catskill Front. Here and there, you will find more vantage points. Soon the trail branches; take the left branch toward "Boulder Rock." It isn't far.

It's an odd name, but a good one; Boulder Rock is an enormous rock. You can't miss it; it's just to the left of the trail. What's perhaps most remarkable about it is that it is perched right on the edge of the cliff. Yawning out before the boulder is a steep 2,000-foot drop. And if Boulder Rock had been any smaller, it would have been pushed over the edge. Alf Evers recorded that virtually all such boulders, which were small enough and close enough to the edge, did meet such a fate. But this one is much too big for even a small army of brawny vandals to dis- · locate.

So fine, now we know why it is still there, but how did such a boulder get there in the first place? The answer is easy, and it is a good one. Boulder Rock is called by geologists a "glacial erratic." Our story takes us back about 14,000 years ago to when the last glacier was advancing down the Hudson Valley. The Ice Age was ending, but ice was still active in the valley. Glaciers are currents of moving ice, and they can pick up and move almost anything they want to, including very large boulders. Boulder Rock was swept up in the flow of ice and carried here. The ice then melted and left the boulder behind.

This is commonplace; many displaced boulders are found throughout glaciated regions. We call them erratics because their lithologies do not match the local bedrock. Boulder Rock isn't all that erratic, however, it probably came from North Mountain, only a few miles away.

Please do make the trip, especially if you have not been to the park before. When you reach Boulder Rock, try to imagine it as it was long ago. Picture the valley, before you, filled with old gray ice. The ice is melting and wet with pools of water. Up here, water is pouring off the ice and Boulder Rock itself is just emerging from its white shroud. All around, the landscape is still pretty bleak. It will be quite a while before this area recovers from its glaciation, but when it does recover, it will have done it very well indeed. You can see the results today.

Woodstock Times, June 1998

GHOSTS AT CLERMONT

A GEOLOGIST never knows when he is about to take a trip into our distant past; it's just part of the job. I began one of those time travels recently when I was visiting the Livingston mansion, Clermont, located on the Hudson. Just north of the visitor's center I saw a fine honey locust tree.

The honey locust is certainly not the greatest of trees; there are bigger and prettier ones. Nevertheless, there is something very special about this species. Honey locusts are "armored" with very dangerous looking spikes. These can be three or four inches long, and often they occur in mean-looking clusters. The biggest of those is found on the lower reaches of the tree's trunk. Up above, there are plenty more strung out on the lower branches.

Brush up against this tree and you will quickly find out what they are for; they are vicious defense mechanisms. The lower branches hang down, and seem to reach out with their spikes as if intending to do harm. Browsing mammals will soon find out, and long remember, the dangers of trying to eat the foliage of this tree.

But who are these spikes defending against? You might guess the white-tailed deer, especially if you are among those who have prized shrubbery in your yard. But white-tailed deer would hardly be bothered by these spikes. They have slender snouts, and they find plenty of space to pick between the spikes. No, locusts have never much worried about deer.

But, if it is not deer, then who or what? There are no other obvious browsers in today's woods so why do the trees go to all that trouble of growing those nasty long spikes? Those spikes, also, had to be aimed at something a lot bigger than a deer. And a lot taller too; they reach up to about 15 feet or so above the ground. There is a real problem here; the fact is that there simply are no big creatures in today's world that threaten our locusts.

The spikes on a honey locust tree. (Titus)

But there were some long ago. Back at the end of the Ice Age, the Hudson Valley did have a great herbivore that might very well have pestered our honey locusts. And it was plenty large enough too. It was the mastodont.

Modern elephants have a bad reputation for tearing up forests. They love to pull down limbs, and they are perfectly capable of stripping bark off the lower trunks of trees as well. In fact, elephants can virtually create their own habitat. They destroy so many trees that they break up the forests, creating lots of meadow in between the remaining patches of woodland.

That rambunctious behavior creates just exactly the right habitat for honey locusts. Locusts like broken forests, preferring to be right on the border between meadow and trees. So, it would seem that evolution had cleverly adapted the locust for life with the mastodonts. These great elephants created the habitat that was just right for locusts. At the same time the spikes protected the locusts from any potential damage from the mastodonts.

And there was more: the honey locust seed pods very likely appealed to the mastodonts. Those seed pods hung just above the spikes; the elephants could just reach beyond the spikes, eat the pods and then deposit the seeds elsewhere within their droppings.

All in all, the mastodonts and honey locusts enjoyed a very fine symbiosis. But then, abruptly, it all ended. The mastodonts went extinct about 11,000 years ago. The locusts lost the elephants that had helped them so much in reproduction. They have survived to this day, but surely they are not as successful as was once the case. Still, in the end, it is quite the concept to contemplate. These trees and their long spikes vigilantly wait for the elephants that will never ever come again. It is only the ghosts of mastodonts that still haunt our forests.

The Independent, May 2004

ABOUT THE PUBLISHER

PURPLE MOUNTAIN PRESS is a publishing company committed to producing the best books of regional interest as well as bringing back into print significant older works. It published Dr. Titus's previous two books: *The Catskills: A Geological Guide* and *The Catskills in the Ice Age*. For a free catalog, write Purple Mountain Press, Ltd., P.O. Box 309, Fleischmanns, NY 12430-0309; or call 845-254-4062; or fax 845-254-4476; or email purple@catskill.net.

http://www.catskill.net/purple